# Sleeping Bags and Tortures

## The Private Diaries of an Adventurous Scout and his Scout Leader

John Hemming-Clark

© Searchline Publishing 2016
First printed 2016

ISBN: 978 1 897864 32 6

Published by Searchline Publishing
Searchline House, Holbrook Lane, Chislehurst, BR7 6PE, UK
Tel & Fax: +44 (0)20 8295 0739
www.inyougo.webeden.co.uk
https://www.facebook.com/SleepingBagsandTortures/

Printed by Catford Print Centre

Scouting and guiding is hard work and it is only because of the
dedication of thousands of adults in the UK and beyond (although
it's only an hour a week) that books like this are possible. So
thank you leaders *et al*. Special thanks to the Chislehurst Scout
groups (my major source material), especial thanks to Christian
Daintith for a couple of splendid contributions; also Suzy
Thaman, Ross Phillips, Alan Bolger, Clare Shadbolt, Debbie
Fullick & Paul Hasling for some great ideas.

John Hemming-Clark is the author of the best-selling *In You Go!
A Year or Two in the Life of a Scout Leader*. *Sleeping Bags and
Tortures* is his second book in a three-part series. He has also
written *1000 Fantastic Scout Games*. All three books are
available from www.inyougo.webeden.co.uk or from Amazon as a
download.

Dedicated to the memory of
Ben Richardson

Also by John Hemming-Clark:

In You Go! A Year or Two in the Life of a Scout Leader
1000 Fantastic Scout Games

www.inyougo.webeden.co.uk

# Introduction

Alex lives in Chislehurst, Kent where he's, so far, been cosseted from the harsh realities of life. He has just moved up to the Scout Section from Cubs and is sooo excited! He has decided to keep a diary of his new adventures.

His Scout leader, John (Skip) also lives in Chislehurst. He has kept a diary for many years. However, more recently his diary has focussed on his Scouting. Not so much the adventures, but the trials and tribulations of being a Scout leader as he recounts the same situations as Alex but through a leader's eyes and not a Scout's, alongside his - sometimes strained - relationships and dealings with Scout parents.

Sleeping Bags and Tortures is three stories in one book: the diary of a Scout, the diary of a Scout leader, and interwoven together the hilarious story of one year in the life of 3rd Chislehurst Scouts.

From Alex's start in the Scout Section, he and John take us on a journey through troop meetings and outdoor activities with much of the summer holiday devoted to a daily diary kept during a trip to the Aosta Valley in Italy on a crazy camp which shows the Scouting spirit at its best.

However, amongst the fun, not all is as it seems. For one person we start to get the impression that the fun is ending and the seriousness of life is beginning, perhaps a little too soon.

Sleeping Bags and Tortures is written in a way that makes it accessible not only to Scouts and leaders, but also to most parents and teenagers (so long as the young people only read Alex's entries and even then with parental guidance), as well as anyone who has ever worked with children and who has an appreciation of the almost larger than life characters that some of them are.

However, it was never intended that these diaries be published, so apologies in advance to anyone who feels offended. They have also been left more or less unaltered in order to preserve an original feel. This does at times mean that Alex's grammar and spelling aren't always as good as is taught in some schools.

This is John Hemming-Clark's second story book, a follow up to his immensely successful "In You Go! A Year or Two in the Life of a Scout Leader."

## Explanations

[] describes a place without naming it.

Some of the names of individuals, places and products have been changed, with Facebook friends suggesting alternatives. Some have been redacted with xxxxx. (However, on one page xxxxx means "five kisses" and not "redacted.") Some haven't been redacted. Many of the incidents described actually happened, some didn't, not in 3rd Chislehurst at least.

```
WARNING:
Do not assume that any of the
activities described in this
book are in any way safe.
```

## Wednesday 31st December
## Skip

In that rather quiet time between Christmas and the New Year I have not been idle, Mr Diary. Every year I write a New Year letter to parents in order to clarify matters that have arisen during the past year, to make sure certain things don't happen again, and to encourage them to think as a team. However, it seems hints really don't seem to work so for this coming year I've had to spell things out a little more explicitly.

Dear parents

Thank you for all your support during this year just past. It has been an exciting time in 3rd Chislehurst. "Living on the edge" should be a Scout motto. One of my favourite examples of this is at our weekly troop meetings. I understand that you may have to wait until I contact you all to say, "Friday's meeting will have to be cancelled unless at least one of you says that you can help," before you realise that you are free, but I do know, of course, that someone will be available despite the fact that I asked for help before the term started, not half-way through. Where it becomes really "edgy" is when you're down to help and then contact me the night before to say, "Sorry, can't help tomorrow – have you got someone else to help?" The answer normally is that there are several parents just waiting to rush down to the Scout Hut, but I'ld rather not tell you or them that; let's wait until an hour before the meeting is due to start so that they're all on tenterhooks, wondering if they're going to be picked that week. A bit like being "on call" – but you're not a doctor. Two hours in the pub with mates, a fantastic meal at the new restaurant in the High Street, next week's shopping perhaps? They can all be put on hold so that you can run down to the Scout Hut and say, "Hi, here I am. You didn't think I would let you down did you?"

Troop meetings
At the end of troop meetings I would be grateful if you would,
1. Pick up your young people, or
2. Arrange for someone else to pick up your young people, or
3. Let me know that they are permitted to go home by themselves.

The troop meeting times are 7pm to 9pm on a Friday. If you drop your young people off at 7.45pm it doesn't mean that you can pick them up at 9.45pm. It will also mean that we are most probably out. Out in the field, out in the woods (one of three), out on the Common. No, I won't be leaving a note on the door. If you are unable / unwilling to pick up your young people at 9pm they will, in future, be sent to [a children's hotel in south London] where they will be looked after extremely well until you are ready to pick them up. No, I won't be paying the bill, even if it is "loads more than a baby-sitter."

Contact numbers
Please ensure that the contact details that I have for you are up to date. When I ask for a telephone number, please don't give your young people's as I don't want to contact them in an emergency – they probably are the emergency. Please write it in such a way as I can read it. Please make sure that it is complete. When the form asks for a second contact number, please don't repeat the first one.

8

## Mobile phones

When I ask that your young people don't bring their phones to troop meetings, it doesn't mean let them bring them and keep them in their pockets. When I confiscate them because their phone has appeared out of their pocket during flag-break (i.e. the first five minutes of the meeting) and they've forgotten to ask for it back at the end of the meeting and so I've taken them home, no I won't be driving round to your houses that night to return them, or tomorrow night or any night - or day. If you come round my house you can have it back if I'm in, otherwise wait until the following Friday. If the summer holidays have just started, forget about it. Give them a Frisbee or a ball or a compass, maybe all three. No, they won't die, they will be fitter and happier.

## Activities

Activities require you to sign an activity information form. Where it says, "Please return this form to John by 26th January" I don't expect to have to add the year. The "return by" date is a final date not a negotiable one. Please do not send your young people to the Scout Hut on the day of the activity and tell me, either

1. That you have filled the form in and given it to me already and I've lost it, especially before I've even said anything about not having a form, or
2. That you have filled the form in but it's at home somewhere, or
3. That you have filled the form in and, "Here it is."

## Payment

If any payment is required I will not book in your young people until it is received. If you have cash-flow issues, tell me. I won't tell anyone, I promise. I will come to a mutually acceptable arrangement so that your young people can take part in the activity. No, I don't know that you were, "always going to pay." If you book and don't pay then 3rd Chislehurst loses the money, no one else.

Camp
If your young people are ill, please don't send them to camp. No, the fresh air won't "do them good," because they will be in a tent with one, three or seven other young people who will catch what they have. Similarly, if we ring you to ask you to come and collect your young people because they are ill, we don't mean at the end of camp, we mean now. If you have snatched a weekend in Paris and are half-way up the Eiffel Tower and you haven't given us an emergency contact locally - No, we are not going to "hold onto them," we're going to take them to hospital and / or 'phone social services. If you reckon that you really must send your ill young people to camp because you have booked a romantic weekend with your spouse in a really expensive hotel and "it will be a complete waste of money if we have to cancel," then take your young people with you.

With best wishes

John / Skip

**Thursday 1st January**
**Skip**
Ugh. Another year. And I'm still here. Scouts goes back tomorrow. I really am getting too old for this, especially as I won't be allowed to get a proper sleep for a second night in a row. If only I was really prepared and kept a survival bag in the shed. Then I could have been just a little bit warmer last

night in the greenhouse. Mind you, my sleeping bag does need replacing; it's getting very old and very, very worn. A bit like me. I should have put one down on my Christmas list. Still, it's a bit late now. Perhaps I'll get one for my birthday although that's not 'til March and I'll probably forget to ask. If I do ask, I must remember to request a normal bag, that means a rectangular one, not these stupid mummified ones that everyone has these days. When you're in your bed you're not pinned down like you're in a straight-jacket and can't move, so why in a sleeping bag? I like to open my legs, move my knees up and down, turn over... all things that my ancient mummy bag won't let me do. What is does let me do is roll over whilst the top of the sleeping bag doesn't move so that when I wake up in the middle of the night, desperate for a pee, I find firstly that my face is in the hood bit so that I think that I'm suffocating, although I could actually be, and secondly that I've corkscrewed myself so well into the inside of the bag that I'm completely stuck. I then have to uncorkscrew myself before I can get out or even get the thing unzipped. Why is it that sleeping bag zips do up easily enough but can't be undone in an emergency? By the time I had worked the zip down and round and down and round because there's no space to roll over in the greenhouse, unless I want to squash the winter cabbages, it was all a bit too late. At least the cabbages won't need watering today. Still, I shouldn't complain too much at my enforced camp as it was nice getting back to nature. However the greenhouse was a bit draughty, and muddy, and smelly, with a puddle in the middle – a bit like the inside of a Scout tent then.

**Thursday 1st January**
**Alex**

A new year and another new Scout arrives at 3rd Chislehurst! Me! What better start to a year?! Scout Scouts starts tomorrow! Not Beaver Scouts, not Cub Scouts, but Scout Scouts. All I wanted for Christmas was Scout stuff. Mummy and daddy bought me a lovely new sleeping bag. I've moved up from "junior" to "adult" so it's a bit long but it means that I can keep all my teddies including Scottie Dog at the bottom as well as loads of sweets when we go on camp. No one will find them down there cos they won't think of looking down there. It's a four seasons bag. This means that I can use it whatever the weather is like. I will be able to take it up mountains when is minus one hundred degrees or sleep in it when it's raining or snowing cos it's waterproof. Daddy said that he would rather have a four seasons hotel but you won't find one of them up Mount Everest. The label also says that it's a mummy sleeping bag. My brother Matthew says that they're called mummy cos they're shaped like a mummified person is inside. These are the best sleeping bags as they mould round you and keep you much warmer than the rectangular ones. I wonder if you can get daddy sleeping bags? Matthew bought me a penknife which is fantastic. It's actually a Swiss Army Knife which is a penknife that the army use so it's got to be good. I've got the Midnite Manager version which has got bits on it that I'm not sure what they are yet. Matthew said that the biggest pocket knife in the world is the Wenger Giant and has over a hundred functions. He says it's a foot long. I bet you couldn't get that in your shirt pocket. Daddy said that he had one once but left it in his trouser pocket and forgot about it. When mummy washed his trousers it disassembled the washing machine. I think he was joking, but I'm not sure. Mine has sixteen functions. I counted them. It's also got a light on the end of it. Auntie Ruth bought me a mug with "Chief Scout" on it. I'm going to take them all to Scouts tomorrow in case we camp the night at the Scout Hut. If not they can be my "show and tell". I'm going to be getting the "out" in "Scout" alright.

## Friday 2nd January
## Skip

Finally made it back indoors. That was some party! So many old mates that I hadn't seen for ages. And such a friendly bunch. It's a pity Julia didn't want to stay out so late, although I have no idea what time she went home – until she told me this evening. I must have followed soon after. I remember singing a romantic lullaby to her outside our bedroom window. I hope she was up there, listening behind the curtains - I wouldn't have wanted Charlie, Hugo and Lucy-Jane to think I was singing it to them. I couldn't manage Scouts tonight. I emailed the parents and told them that I was sick. Hopefully I didn't forget anyone. "Sick of your kids," I should've said. I assume I didn't say it. Come to think of it, I'm not too sure that I didn't. Never mind, that'll thin the numbers out a bit.

## Friday 2nd January
## Alex

No Scouts tonight, no camp, no nothing. No sleeping bag required, no penknife needed, "Chief Scout" mug no use. It's a Friday so why wasn't Scouts on tonight? Mummy said that I was moving up from Cubs to Scouts in the New Year and that it was now on Friday evenings. Mummy said that if I was really bothered I could ring Hugo's dad up to find out why we hadn't heard anything. So I did. However Hugo answered the 'phone and said that his dad had emailed everyone. Fat lot of good that was, seeing as mummy hasn't looked at her emails since Christmas. Hugo said that his daddy was in no fit state to have run Scouts this evening. Apparently his dad had gone out two nights ago and had only just got back indoors. I asked Hugo if he had been on a night hike. Hugo said that it was nothing like that. Apparently, although his dad had returned home yesterday in the early hours he had only been allowed back indoors this morning, having spent last night and the night before in the garden in a "bivi shelter". When I asked Hugo what a bivi shelter was he said that it was like a kind of survival shelter. So I said, "Cool. You're dad's a really great Scout leader isn't he, leading by example, testing out the shelters before we have a go?" Hugo then explained that his dad hadn't planned to do a night and a bit's camping at zero minus degrees in the greenhouse but that his mum had locked him out when he got home at five o'clock in the morning singing, "You'll never get to Heaven in Akela's bra," which is apparently part of a popular Scout camp song. Quite why his dad should be shut out for over a day for practising his singing, especially his Scout singing, I've no idea. Maybe he was a little out of tune.

**Wednesday 7th January**
**Skip**
Never again. Never again. Never again. Having planned to plan next year's Scout programme before Christmas I am now one week into a new year and still nothing's been done. I even had an extra Friday off last week. This is no way to run Scouts. No more drinking from now on. I emailed the parents to remind them that Scouts will reconvene on the 9th. I have a couple of new ones starting - Joe xxxxx and Alex xxxxx. Hopefully, they'll be a bit more keen than some of the ones I've had recently. We'll see. No doubt they'll turn

14

up with new Scout shirts that will be big enough for me to fit into. "He's going to be with you for four years, so he'll grow into it," they'll say. In my experience they leave Scouts at fourteen having either never grown into it or grown out of it after about three months. Hugo told me that I need to learn some new Scout songs, not that I thought I knew any in the first place.

## Wednesday 7th January
## Alex
Scouts is on this Friday! Hurrah! At last! Mummy's now reading her emails and she's had another one from Hugo's dad to say that we are to turn up at the Scout Hut at 7pm prompt. I'm allowed to wear my Cub top until Hugo's dad invents me after a few weeks. This way, Hugo's dad said to mummy, that if I don't like Scouts, mummy won't have wasted the money on a new shirt. Don't like Scouts!? I have a Chief Scout mug. Doesn't his dad know that I'm desperate to become a Scout? Beavers was good, Cubs was great but I'm now ten and five months and ready to "put myself about a bit," which is what Hugo said his daddy was doing last week (according to his mummy) which led to his unplanned garden camp. Gosh, in that case I reckon I could make quite a good Scout leader myself when I'm old enough. I'm obviously on the right tracks already. I must remember to tell Hugo's dad on Friday that I'm ready to put myself about a bit as well. I bet he'll be impressed!

## Friday 9th January
## Skip
Well, that wasn't too bad after all. The two new boys were fine although the Alex chap is a bit keen. Just like his brother. He told me that he wanted to be invented quickly.

15

When I asked what he wanted to be invented as he said, "A Scout". I told him that he was a Scout already, although only a Cub Scout for the time being. He came loaded with a sleeping bag that he wouldn't let go of all evening. Maybe he thought we were doing a sleepover. The ice-breaker was fun and gave Alex a chance to chat to Tegan. I'll have to keep my eye on those two. They were making everyone laugh. Apparently Sarah-Jane's named her pony after a brothel in Cologne. Can't think how that got past her parents. We did a bit of emergency first aid and played a couple of games. Joe got a bump on his head as he was running around a bit too fast and then fell over and hit the first-aid box. At least he knew where to find the cool packs. After flag down I asked Alex and Joe if they had enjoyed their first Scout meeting and Alex said something really odd. I don't know who he's been talking to, although – on second thoughts - I may have a good idea. I told Joe and Alex about the Bromley District Challenge that includes having to camp in each month. They looked a bit puzzled for some reason. Maybe they're not going to be up to it.

## Friday 9th January
## Alex

At last! I'm a Scout! Not an official Scout Scout, still only a Cub Scout, but I told Hugo's dad, who we have to call "John" or "Skip," that I want to be invented as soon as possible. I'm going to call Hugo's dad "Skip" as that's his proper name. We were told that we need to learn the Scout Promise. I've already learnt it. "On my honour, I promise to do my duty to God and to the Queen, to help other people and to keep the Scout Law" so I'm not going to need any prompting. Now Skip tells me that there are other Promises that I could make. There's a Promise for people who don't believe in

16

God. I was talking to a girl called Chloe. She said that she made the Scout Promise although she doesn't believe in God. She said that if you don't believe in God then what's the problem in making a Promise to something that doesn't exist? She said that she coughed when she said "God" so it didn't count anyway. Apparently she also added onto the end of her Promise, "And to try and do it all better than my sister did" which I don't think is legal either. She said that there's a Scout group in Bromley who add all sorts of things onto their Promise. She reckons they've even got a Pirate's Promise. There's a Hindu Promise, a Muslim Promise, a Jewish Promise and a Sikh Promise. This is getting really confusing. I don't know which Promise I'm going to make. Maybe I'll choose a different one. Skip said Scouts is inclusive which means we involve everybody. Joe is a new Scout as well and he told Skip that he is a Jedi and so wants to make the Jedi Promise. Skip told him that there wasn't a Jedi Promise so Joe said that that wasn't very inclusive was it? Sarah-Jane then said that if she knew that there was a choice that she would have made the Pascha Promise. She told Skip that that was the name of her pony. Then she explained that Pascha means Resurrection and her pony nearly died when it was a baby. After all the talk about being on a Promise we had to ask the Scout next to us what their favourite food was as a "bit of an ice-breaker." I started to talk to a nice girl called Tegan. She has hair down to her waist. Maybe it's her religion. I reckon that it's going to seriously get in the way when she's putting herself about a bit. I didn't tell her that though. She told me that her favourite food is Baked Alaska. I told her that wasn't really funny as an ice-breaker food but she insisted that Baked Alaska really was a food. She's obviously not been a Scout for very long. She then said, "Okay then, Arctic Roll." I told

17

her that was stupid as well. When Skip asked us what our neighbour's favourite food was I said, with a sigh, that Tegan's was Baked Alaska and Arctic Roll. The other Scouts laughed and I so said that I knew they didn't exist but I was just repeating what she had said. Then they laughed again.

We then started work on our badges. We're going to be doing the emergency aid badge. We learnt "Dr A B" which stands for Danger, Response, Airway and Breathing. Skip says that this is the order in which you assess a casualty. We learnt that cuts equal plasters, burns equal cold water and bumps equal ice pack. We then played a game of cat and mouse which is quite dangerous. I think Skip was trying to get an emergency so that we could practice Dr A B. One Scout chases another up and down lines of Scouts with their arms outstretched. They then all change direction with their arms so that rows become columns and columns become rows. This can turn the tables on whoever is or was winning. It was a bit unfair though because whilst Tegan was playing the cat, the mouse was played by Joe, who is quite small. Joe just kept taking short cuts under outstretched arms when Skip wasn't looking. When he did it near me I stuck my foot out and he tripped over, obviously. However, he was going at quite some speed so managed to launch himself out of the game and bashed his head quite hard on a fire extinguisher. As he lay in a heap on the floor with a large bump appearing on his forehead, Tegan shouted out, "Has anybody got some Arctic Roll?!" All the Scouts laughed. Again. Except for me. I went and found an ice pack and Skip put it on Joe's swollen forehead. The only downside this evening was at the end at flag down when Skip asked me if I had enjoyed myself. I told him that it was a fabulous evening and that I was starting to put myself about a bit like I had been told he had been doing recently. He went all red and then said that that was fine, even for a boy of my age, but that I was to promise that it would stop once I got married. However, seeing as I'm never going to get married this isn't going to be a problem and I can go on putting myself about a bit for the rest of my life, even when I'm really, really old, like he is. I didn't tell him that though. P.S. I didn't need my sleeping bag and there was no show and tell.

Skip has said that we can all start the Bromley District Challenge. This involves lots of challenges and to get gold we have to sleep in every month. Can't see that that's a problem seeing as I sleep in every day. Our first camp is at the Scout Hut next Saturday so long as mummy signs a form. I'm going to get gold before I'm an Explorer.

**Saturday 10th January**
**Alex**
Apparently Baked Alaska and Arctic Roll are both foods. However, as they both contain ice cream I can't imagine why anyone would have them as their favourite food, especially in January.

**Thursday 15th January**
**Skip**
Another night of having to do no preparation as the District has arranged for as many as want to to go to St Bart's [school] to hear famous adventurer James Ketchell give a talk tomorrow. I wonder what it is with these parents? Thirty-six Scouts, thirty-six emails and only one reply. I now have only one Scout going. A very poor show.

**Friday 16th January**

## Alex

No Scout meeting tonight as we went instead to St Bart's to see a man called James Ketchell who talked to us and inspired us to greatness. There were loads of Scouts there as this was what is called a district event. This means that more Scouts can go. There were twenty of us from 3rd Chislehurst which is quite a good turnout although I was the only one who had a place reserved at the front. It said, Alex xxxxx, 3rd Chislehurst on a piece of paper which was on a chair. This was because they knew that I am a future Chief Scout. The others had to sit at the back. James has rowed the Atlantic Ocean, climbed Mount Everest and cycled around the world. However he is twenty-something years old so he's had plenty of time to do all these things. I'm going to do them all whilst / when I'm still a teenager. We had an opportunity to ask him questions. Sarah-Jane asked him what his favourite place was and he turned the question around and asked Sarah-Jane the same thing. She said, "New York." James said that that was cool and when had she been there? Sarah-Jane then said that she hadn't been there but if she did go then she reckons she would really like it. What a daft girl she is. That's like saying that your favourite food is cavalier even though no one's ever eaten any apart from Russians. She told James that she was going to go there by pony. Then someone asked her what her pony's name was and 3rd Chislehurst, from the back row, shouted "Pascha" and some of the grown-ups smiled. I don't know why. I wanted to ask James what his favourite food was but given that he had climbed Mount Everest I thought that he would probably say "Baked Alaska" or something stupid like that and so I didn't ask. Joe's dad was there and he asked if James was going to be the next Chief Scout and James just laughed. As well he might! As far as I'm concerned I'm going to be the next Chief Scout AND whilst still a teenager. Not that I'm a teenager yet. But I soon will be. Just two years, six months, two weeks and four days to go.

## Friday 16th January
## Skip

Surprise, surprise. Twenty Scouts decided to turn up, nineteen having forgotten to tell me. At 9pm, when they were supposed to be picking up, only new Scout Alex's mum and Joe's dad were there. Then, at 9.20, just as I was about to ring Social Services, they all rolled in. Apparently they had all been in the Bricklayers Arms. By the sounds and smells of it they had been having quite a good time. Tegan's mum said that she would be taking Sarah-Jane home as Sarah-Jane's dad was still in the pub and, "is quite happy in there". Tomorrow we have a sleepover at the hut. I mustn't forget my (old - and muddy) sleeping bag.

## Saturday 17th January
## Alex

An extra Scout meeting tonight which was actually a Scout camp at the hut! We had Crusher staying with us. Crusher is Trudy's dad. Crusher is his real name. His pretend name is Oliver. Skip said that Crusher is an asshole. Skips and Crushers are people on a ship and we are all the crew. We're in a petrol tent, which sounds a bit dangerous. They can sleep eight Scouts and there are six Scouts in mine. We learnt how to build a fire using tinder, kindling and logs which Skip had brought along. To remember the order Skip said we should use amenimic which is an aide memoire. I don't really know what he was talking about so I just watched but Try Kissing Lotte is important for some reason.

I'm not kissing Lotte, I'm kissing Tegan if anyone. However, she's a petrol leader so she's quite old. We cooked sosages on sticks over our fire. All the sosages went black which we thought was cooked enough but when Joe bit into his it was still cold and raw on the inside. Joe said that it didn't matter cos if they were cooked on the outside that was okay and so ate it. Then Skip came out and I showed him my sosage. He cut it open and said that it wasn't cooked and that it was just as well that I hadn't eaten it. I asked what would happen if I ate it and he said that I would die. He then said that if I tried to cook it any more then it would be too hard to bite into and so he would finish them all off in the microwave. He then asked Joe where his sosage was. He said that he had dropped it in the fire. It's unfortunate that he didn't cos at least then it would have been cooked. Instead he's going to die. Once they were finished off in the microwave we put them in buns with loads of ketchup and they were yummy. Tegan said that she loved sosages and I said I did as well. Any girl who likes a sosage can be my girlfriend.

Sarah-Jane is a vegetarian which means she doesn't eat meat, but I bet she would if she was really hungry, even Pascha. I wonder if you can eat pony? Sarah-Jane had a vegetarian sosage. Actually she had five cos there were six in a box and Sarah-Jane only wanted one. But then Joe had one. He didn't want one but Skip made him have it cos he said that Joe would be hungry. Sarah-Jane's sosage wasn't on a stick, it was in a pan of hot water on the fire. I asked Sarah-Jane why a vegetarian sosage was sosage shaped, why wasn't it flat like a burger or round like a scotch egg but she said she didn't know and didn't even care. What she did say, though, was that the first vegetarian sosage was called a Cologne sausage. Skip then said that there were probably loads of those around, even today, then chuckled to himself. I don't know why it's so funny. I thought Sarah-Jane was being very clever. I asked Skip when the first meat sosage was invented and he said, "At the dawn of time," which is stupid cos at the dawn of time there was not much around, specially not sosages. Then Joe was sick. He's had to go home. This is good news as it means that there are now only five of us in the petrol tent which means a bit more room.

Before hot chocolate time we had a game of hide and seek in the woods. Skip and Crusher were hopeless. I know they told us to hide well and not to make any noise but it took them hours to find us. By the time that they started to work out where we all were it was getting really late. I thought that we weren't going to be able to get to bed at all before our mummies and daddies came to pick us up. I had hidden in a great place. I was almost inside a huge hollow log. I was there all on my own in the darkest part of the wood, but I was getting really scared and there were strange noises. I thought maybe I was going to be forgotten and no one would find me. I started to cry. Then I heard Skip so I stood up and waved my arms so that he could find me easily, which he did, thank goodness.

We were allowed to bring a small packet of sweets each which we're supposed to hand in for Skip to dish out, but no one does hand them in. Or if they do they just hand in a few and keep the rest. Skip didn't ask me so I have a Dairy Milk bar in my sleeping bag. It says it's 850g whatever that means. Huge is what I would call it. Someone brought it round to our house at Christmas but no one had eaten any so I've got it. I unwrapped it and was going to give some to Skip but then he would know that there was more so I've decided not to tell him, or anyone else. It is in a paper wrapper and then in foil. I don't know why chocolate always has foil round it. Maybe it has to be kept warm. I couldn't get the silver wrapper back on properly so I've just put it back in the paper wrapper and put it down the bottom of my sleeping bag with Scottie Dog. It will keep nice and warm down there. I've stuck the foil down there as well. If we're going to need some silver foil for cooking then I'm Prepared!

## Saturday 17th January
## Skip
The sleepover is going fine, so far. Fortunately one of my new Assistant Scout Leaders, otherwise known as an ASL, Oliver, is staying as well. I went through the fire-lighting stages of Tinder, Kindling and Logs. To help them remember the order I said that it's, "T K L" or "Try Kissing Lotte." Once the fire was going well the Scouts were all given a sausage on a stick to cook. I told them that the secret was to rotate the sausage above the embers but most of them thought that the more heat and flame the better so most of the sausages went black on the outside and uncooked on the inside. No one ate one. Joe had a veggie sausage because he dropped his pork one in the fire. Then he was sick so I sent him home. His mother wasn't best pleased when I phoned her up to tell her the bad news. She said, "But I'm at the theatre." "Being operated on?" I heard myself saying. "No, John. I'm at Die Fledermaus." "Well, you've got out of jail," I told her. I don't think she got the operatic connection. "Can't you quarantine him?" she asked in her hoity-toity voice. I told her, "Our Scout Hut is an old stables not a fully-admitting hospital. I know what I'll do, I'll 'phone social services." "I'm on my way," was her immediate reply. That's one way of getting the necessary response. I expect

she's known to social services anyway. I wouldn't have normally minded but she hasn't even paid Joe's subs yet for Cubs last term at his old Scout group let alone this term's subs here. Maybe that's why he moved. Keep the subs not paid for a term and then move on. Gosh, if she did that in just Bromley district she could keep going until Joe was in his mid twenties! She eventually turned up at about half-past-eleven just as hot chocolate was being consumed round the camp fire. It was a bit late but the Scouts were still talking excitedly about yesterday's James Ketchell visit. He seems to have inspired some of them at least. When Joe's mum appeared she was walking - or rather tottering - down the path to the Scout Hut in very high heels, wearing an expensive perfume and a skinned animal fur round her neck. Barnaby asked her if she would like to roast it in the embers but she told him, rather too sternly I thought, that "It's only the fur." Then Sarah-Jane joined in. She stuck a burnt sausage in her direction and said, "Well, here's the rest of the animal round your neck." "I don't think she's wearing pig," I reminded Sarah-Jane before things got too ugly with my pre-pubescent animal activists.

Sarah-Jane decided to tell the Scouts that vegetarian sausages started in Cologne. I told Oliver that there were no doubt plenty of those still around, especially in Pascha, and he grinned. At least he has a sense of humour.

To give ourselves a bit of a rest we sent the Scouts off for a game of hide and seek. We told them to hide well and keep quiet and the last one to be found would be the winner. Oliver and I then sat down together for nice cup of coffee and got chatting. Unfortunately we forgot all about the Scouts who had been hiding for at least half an hour so we had to go and try to find them. They were all chatting and shining their torches. We found Alex first, but he'll soon learn that you can't easily hide if you're standing up behind a tree stump waving your torch in your hands and shouting, "Over here!" He looked as though he had been crying so I asked him what the matter was and he said that it was hay-fever. This is a bit odd for January and, in any event, his mother hadn't put it on his form, so I don't know what was going on but he seemed okay and didn't appear to have been suffering. It didn't look as though he had been bitten or cut so I didn't pursue the matter.

**Sunday 18th January**
**Alex**
The day didn't get off to a very good start. Somehow I managed to slide down my sleeping bag in the night and cos it's adult size and not junior there was quite a way to slide. When I woke up I thought I was being suffocated so I screamed. A boy in my tent called Josh rescued me. He unzipped my bag like it was a bananana and opened it up so that I could escape but before I had a chance he screamed and said, "Urrrgh, Yuch! You've sweary word yourself in your pyjamas". I hadn't but I suppose it looked like I had cos I had chocolate all over Scottie Dog and all round my pyjama bottoms. I told Josh that it was only chocolate and he said, "Yeah – milk, milk, lemonade, round the corner chocolate drops". He even had some actions to go with it which didn't look very nice. I told him that it was chocolate and it was Dairy Milk that I had hidden in my sleeping bag and then he said that that wasn't very nice cos we're supposed to share it and I hadn't. So I told him that I would've done but that I was keeping it warm and he just laughed. I was trying not to cry but mummy was going to be

so cross. I took my pyjamas off and got dressed with the chocolate still on my feet and went to find Skip. I explained that I had a small bar of chocolate in my sleeping bag by mistake and it had melted in the bag and made a mess and what should I do? Skip just said, "Lick it" which wasn't very helpful. I told him that there was eight hundred and fifty g of it and so he then said, "Scrape it then and we can have a chocolate bacon fondue," which was even less helpful.

For breakfast we had to cook our own meal on our fire that we had got going ourselves. First we had to go and get some Kissing Lotte. That means kindling and logs. We didn't need any Try cos the fire was still hot from last night so we just had to get it going again. The mummies and daddies were told to come and get us at nine o'clock but at nine o'clock we were still gathering kindling and logs from Pond Wood so Skip sent them all home again and told them to come back at ten o'clock. At ten o'clock we were just getting the fire going again (cos in the meantime it had gone out completely) so Skip had to send all the parents home again and told them to come back at twelve o'clock by which time he said that we would definitely be finished. We had bacon, eggs and beans which we had to cook backwards, according to Crusher and he gave me some silver foil. I folded the foil in three, as instructed, and was then told to work it out. Fortunately we were given a tin opener. I opened the beans and poured them onto the foil. They started to run and so I folded the silver foil up a bit. Then I put two bits of bacon on top and then put one egg on top of the bacon. Then I folded the foil over and turned round to try to put the parcel on the fire with my hands behind my back. Crusher asked me what I was doing and I told him that I was trying to put my cooking on the fire backwards. He just smiled and said that I could do frontwards cooking, which was a relief. I suppose doing your cooking backwards makes sure that you don't burn your face if you get too close to the fire which is very sensible. Once all the Scouts had put their silver packages on the fire they all got muddled up cos no one had put their names on the silver foil. After a few minutes I took one off that I thought was mine but it wasn't cos it had eight slices of bacon in it and nothing else. Anyway I ate it cos I was hungry and couldn't really put it back. It was quite tasty. Then there was a big upset cos Sarah-Jane couldn't find her vegetarian bacon. I asked her what it looked like and she said, "It looks like bacon, stupid". Well I'm not stupid and why would vegetarian bacon look like proper bacon like from a pig or a pony? So I asked her. She said that vegetarian bacon came first but I bet it wasn't at the dawn of time. Then Josh opened up his parcel and started to laugh. He said, "Someone's put an egg in here without cracking it!" and then everyone laughed. I laughed as well so that no one would know that that is my parcel. Or should I say was. Then Skip said that at least it would be cooked, which it was, although there was quite a lot of shell in Josh's beans, but he'll survive, unlike Jake.

Crusher told us that at least someone (that means me, although they don't know) didn't put their egg in the microwave and Skip laughed, probably cos it would cook too quickly. Jake is Hawks' petrol leader and he fished out his silver parcel although it had only been on the fire for a few seconds. He ate the raw bacon and said that he liked his meat raw. Jake had put his bacon, beans and eggs in separate parcels and didn't know which ones his egg and beans were in. Anyway, he said he wasn't hungry as he had already eaten a packet of Coco Pops.

28

There was then another drama when Skip asked me where the rest of my tin of beans was. Apparently we were supposed to share the tins of beans one tin for three Scouts, but I had cooked all of them so I did what Joe said last night. So I said that I had dropped the tin in the fire. Skip peered into the fire and said that he couldn't see the tin. I told him that it had probably melted. This time he didn't smile, he just tut-tutted. So some Scouts didn't get any beans, but I didn't either cos Josh got everyone's. After we had finished cooking we had to put our petrol tent down and fold it away. Then we washed up and waited for our mummies and daddies to come and pick us up. At a quarter past twelve Skip started texting the parents and by about one o'clock they had all turned up, apart from Sarah-Jane's dad who was still at work, according to Tegan's mum. This was a bit odd cos I thought he was a teacher so I don't know what teaching he was doing on a Sunday morning. So Sarah-Jane went home with Tegan. Then Jake was sick.

Mummy said that she wondered what Scores on the Doors star rating we had at the Scout Hut. I said that I would ask Skip.

## Sunday 18th January
## Skip
We got the Scouts up at 7am to collect some wood. This should have taken about half an hour but I had to put pick up back to lunch time to give the Scouts time to get enough wood, get their fire going, cook their meal, eat it and clear up. I'm sure if I left the Scouts to it on camp it would take all day just to prepare, eat and clear up three meals with no time left over for anything else.

Alex came and told me that he had pooed himself in the night. To be precise he said that he had had a small bar of chocolate in his sleeping bag but it had melted. However, that wouldn't have been a problem given that chocolate's double wrapped, so he was probably just trying to avoid any embarrassment. I should have gone and found a bucket and mop and some disinfectant but there was no way that I was going to start mopping up poo, first thing in the morning, from a child and his sleeping bag so I told him to lick it up. I hope that he didn't.

Tegan's mother confided in me that Sarah-Jane's father was in the pub and they couldn't get him out so I sent Sarah-Jane home with Tegan. They seemed to be getting on okay after last term's incident with the plastic frog. Having given the four girls two two-man tents why they thought it was sensible to have one as their changing area and then all sleep in the other one, I've no idea. Poor Sarah-Jane said to me this morning that in the middle to the night she needed to go to the toilet. She found that she was sandwiched between two of the other girls and had to pull on the end pole to ease herself out of her sleeping bag. This led to the collapse of the tent entrance. What was worse was that she realised that she had left all her clothes in the other tent so had to find her boots, put them on, negotiate the collapsed entrance, walk to the other tent, go in, get dressed and go to the toilet. Then do it all again in reverse. Maybe they'll think it through a bit better next time.

When Alex's mother turned up I asked her if Alex suffered from hay-fever. She said, "What, in January?" looking at me as if I was mad. I said, rather too meekly, that I thought that it was a bit odd. But I didn't want her to think that Alex had been upset so I didn't say anything more.

I was just clearing up when Jake was suddenly sick. Gavin, his father then told him that he wouldn't be able to get in his car smelling of sick and what was I going to do about it? I decided to employ Friday evening's tactic: "I'll ring social services." "I'll take him in the car." was Gavin's immediate reply. This social services lark is quite a good one. I wonder how many Chislehurst parents really are known to social services?! I should get their number just in case I really do need to get a child picked up. That would be quite funny.

## Monday 19th January
### Alex

Today was not a very good day in the history of Alex Scouting. I have been a Scout Scout nineteen days and I thought that I would put into practice what I had learnt on Scout camp (that is to say sleepover at the Scout Hut). I decided that I would make my own breakfast as this is something that I can now do. I got up really early while everyone else was still asleep and went downstairs into the kitchen. It was still dark outside. I couldn't find any bacon or beans and I certainly wasn't going to make porridge as I always have porridge in the winter and it's really boring except when I put Marmite in it. I did find eggs though. There was box of them in the fridge. As I wasn't going to have anything else cos there wasn't anything I decided to have three eggs for my breakfast. I put them in the microwave and pressed full power for ten minutes as I thought that would be enough and then went to my bedroom to get my FoSpoKn (which is a fork, spoon and knife all in one) that I hide under my pillow so that Matthew

31

can't find it. While I was in my room I heard an enormous explosion and then mummy started screaming. Now what was I to do? Maybe I was going to have to have porridge and Marmite for breakfast after all. I thought that daddy ought to be able to sort it out better than me so I got back into bed and turned off the light. I listened carefully as daddy went downstairs saying, slowly and very clearly and firmly, "I'M - COMING - DOWN - NOW!" but he seemed to take rather a long time to do so as he said it several times. Then it was really quiet and then I heard him coming back up the stairs. He opened my door so I shut my eyes. He didn't turn the light on but whispered, "Alex." I didn't say anything so he shut the door and went back into his bedroom. I couldn't hear what mummy and daddy were saying and I went back to sleep. At least daddy hadn't been killed. I thought that I wouldn't be asleep for very long but after I had got up I found out that the explosion had happened at about one o'clock in the morning, so I wouldn't have been very popular if I had had my breakfast and had then woken daddy up so that he could take me to school. In any case why was mummy awake? If she had been asleep she probably wouldn't have heard anything.

In the morning, I mean the getting-up time of the morning, I went downstairs and found mummy washing the floor. She said that daddy thought that we might've had a bugler but I wasn't to worry and that Matthew must have wanted to cook some eggs and had put them in the microwave, although he had denied it. I said that I had heard a bit of a noise and mummy said that there had been a very loud explosion and she and daddy thought that someone might have broken in. When I asked her what had happened, she told me that you can't put eggs in the microwave unless you've cracked them

32

or pierced the shell, "otherwise that happens" she added, pointing to the microwave door that was now hanging on by just one hinge. I may have to tell her that it was me, but it's not really my fault. How was I to know? I blame Crusher. He didn't say that the microwave would blow up.

## Friday 23rd January
**Alex**

Tonight I was put in my new petrol. I'm a Woodpecker. This is a bit naff. If I'm going to be a boring bird like a Woodpecker then all the other petrols should be boring birds. But they're not. The other petrols are proper birds like Eagles, Hawks and Ravens. I'm not going to make a fuss although I did tell Skip that maybe the petrols should be smaller and nicer birds seeing as we had girls as well. He asked me for some suggestions so I told him the names of some of the little birds that come and visit us on the bird table and he just smiled. We do have a Woodpecker in our garden but I didn't tell him that. I've found out that I can buy all the Scout badges online so I'm going to buy a Kestrel badge. No one will know. Mummy's scout leader friend is called "Kestrel" in her scout group so there must be a badge. My petrol leader is Tegan. She looks a bit like a woodpecker and she also sounds like one with her chatter, chatter like she's tapping into a tree bark for some grubs. The assistant patrol leader is Josh. Or should I say, was Josh. He's not assistant patrol leader just at the moment due to "an incident" last term. That's all that Skip told us but someone must know why he's been demoted. I'll find out sometime.

I asked Skip what star rating we had for Scores on the Doors and he said that he didn't know what I was talking about so we probably have no stars or we've not yet been inspected.

Everywhere that serves food has to be inspected. Even Buckingham Palace has been inspected.

## Friday 23rd January
## Skip

I managed to get the patrols sorted out this evening without too much difficulty. Tegan's been moved up to patrol leader and Josh has been temporarily demoted after the incident with the thunder flash before Christmas. At least I got to the bottom of it eventually. When we played the Raid! wide game out the back I gave them all one smoke grenade and or one thunder flash each. How Josh could think that I would believe him when he said he thought he had a smoke grenade when he actually had a thunder flash, I've no idea. In any event, why putting even a smoke grenade down the toilet would have been a good idea is still beyond me. However, the toilet bowl has been replaced and Josh's dad has a bill waiting for him when he eventually comes home. Joe and Alex have been put into Woodpeckers. I don't think Alex is too impressed so I asked him what patrol he would have if he had the choice. "I've always liked great tits," was his innocent reply. How I managed not to laugh, I don't know. He's staying in Woodpeckers.

## Saturday 24th January
## Alex

I've emailed the Scores on the Doors people to tell them that our Scout Hut needs to be inspected. I also told them that several Scouts had been sick cos they had eaten uncooked food but they hadn't died. Well not yet, cos we've all got to die sometime, but not from eating one of Joe's sosages.

## Friday 30th January

## Alex

Skip told us tonight that we're going to do a camp in March and that it will be run by our local district. It's going to be over two weekends and at the end we will have earned our Outdoors Challenge Award which is one of the big badges that we have to get before we can be Chief Scout. We're going to be sleeping in tents again and that the sleepover camp a couple of weeks ago was just a practice. Thank goodness for that. If it had been a proper camp and we were in the middle of the jungle or up Mount Everest it would be no good eating raw sosage or bacon or having liquid chocolate all over your pyjamas cos there would be no parents to come and rescue you not that Sarah-Jane's parents bothered to rescue her anyway. For all they care she could still be at the Scout Hut trying to light the fire. I'm going to start preparing for the challenge now as James said the other week that preparation was the key to success. From now on I'm going to sleep in my new sleeping bag. I won't tell mummy. I don't expect that she would let me. I unrolled it tonight and put it under my bed. Once mummy had said "goodnight" I got out of bed, pulled the sleeping bag out from under the bed and put it on my bed and climbed into it. It felt very cosy. Then I thought that I would need to mess my bed up a bit otherwise mummy would wonder why I hadn't slept in it. So I got out of my sleeping bag, took it off the bed, took my duvet off the bed, put my sleeping bag on the sheets, put the duvet back on and climbed into the sleeping bag again. However I was then too hot so I got out of my sleeping bag, got the duvet off and put that under the bed. Then I got back into my sleeping bag. I then thought that maybe I was a bit too cosy and that when I go camping I won't have a nice mattress underneath me, just some wet grass so I decided that I would sleep in my sleeping bag on the floor. So I got out of my sleeping bag again and put it on the floor alongside my bed and got in again. I then started to write my diary for the day.

## Friday 30th January
## Skip

This evening we started to prepare for the Outdoor Challenge Award weekend that is coming up next month. Fortunately it's arranged by the district so not much planning on my part is required. I've said that I will help but apart from that, all I have to do is arrange a few tents and turn up, then spend the weekend wandering around with my hands behind my back looking busy. Re-sult!

## Saturday 31st January
## Morning
## Alex

It was a bit odd leaning against a bedside table to write my diary and it wasn't very comfortable so I climbed out of the sleeping bag again, left it on the floor and climbed back into bed, then I found my duvet was under the bed. So I got off the bed, found the duvet, put it on the bed and climbed back in. Then I fell asleep. By the time I fell asleep it was probably morning. Oh well, better luck tonight.

## Saturday 31st January
## Evening
## Alex

Mummy came into my room this morning whilst I was waking up and wanted to know why my sleeping bag was on the floor. I told her that I wanted to get used to unpacking it and packing it up again so that I would be able to when I was on camp. She then wanted to know in that case why I

36

hadn't packed it up. I explained that I wasn't going to pack it up straight after unpacking it as I wanted to give it time it to fluff itself up before putting it back as it wouldn't be so easy then and I wanted to try to put it back under extreme conditions. James has had to go camping in extreme conditions and he wouldn't be very prepared if he hadn't tried to stimulate extreme conditions when putting his sleeping bag in its little bag carrier thing. But he is prepared so he would have practised and that is what I am going to do. Mummy then asked if I was going to pack my sleeping bag up tonight and I told her that I was going to sleep in it first, like I would on camp. I wasn't sure what she was going to say and I thought that she might say "no" or tell me off, but she just said "cool" and went downstairs. I suppose I should practice packing it up in somewhere smaller than my bedroom cos when I'm on camp I'm going to be in a tent so not much space so what I need to do is practice in somewhere that's confined. When I was going up to bed tonight mummy asked if I was still going to be sleeping in my sleeping bag and I said "yes" and she didn't say anything and so I asked her if it was okay and she said "yes" so I asked her why she didn't mind. She said that it would mean less washing. I don't know if she meant me or the sleeping bag, but I didn't ask. I went and got it out of my room and took it into mummy's wardrobe cos it's a bit bigger than mine but still quite small like a tent. I then tried to pack it in my sleeping bag bag but it was very difficult. You have to sort of stuff it in then push it and squeeze it and push some more and it was dark but I managed it and then I pulled the draw string at the top and it was done. Hurray! I was very pleased to get out of mummy's wardrobe cos it was full of her clothes and very clostraphobic. I got back into my bedroom and opened up my sleeping bag bag and pulled my sleeping bag out and also I seemed to have packed two of mummy's dresses as well. I was just wondering how I was going to put them back without mummy finding out when she walked in and looked at me and my sleeping bag and my sleeping bag bag and her two dresses and just said, "I hope you're not going to get into those as well?" Well of course I wasn't cos they're too big but they do smell quite nice.

## Saturday 31st January
## Skip
Got a 'phone call from the district to tell me that I had been put down for first aid demos and safety with lamps and stoves at the Outdoor Challenge Award weekend and would I mind bringing several first aid kits plus extra bandages, plasters, slings, sterile gloves, stoves, gas, various lamps – enough for seventy Scouts. So much for a weekend wandering around with my hands behind my back looking busy. Fortunately Julia will be able to get her hands on some first aid stuff from the hospital.

## Sunday 1st February
## Alex
I didn't sleep very well last night. Every time I rolled over in my sleep I woke up. It was a bit odd having a hard floor to sleep on, but that's what it's going to be like when I'm on camp. Or in prison. Josh's dad's in prison. Mind you, the way that Josh behaves at Scouts I'm surprised that he's not in prison with him. I don't know why he's in prison. Tegan told me that he is but she doesn't know why. I'm going to keep sleeping in my sleeping bag even though it's uncomfortable. And chocolaty, even though mummy has washed it. More than once, she said. I'm sure I'll get used to it.

I've been a Scout for a whole month now and Skip is going to invent me this Friday.

I pinched and punched, first day of the month Matthew at breakfast. He told me that if I ever did it again he was going to tell mummy who blew up the microwave. This is called blackmail. He then made me promise never to do it again. He said that if I didn't promise he would hit me. This is also blackmail, sort of. I wasn't very happy cos he shouldn't be threatening me and anyway, he used to always pinch and punch me. This was the first day I managed to do it first so I was really happy and I can't see why he should mind. Anyway, I promised not to pinch and punch him. In fact I did more than that. I said, On my honour, I promise that I will not pinch, I will not punch, on the first day of the month, ever again. Then he said good. Then he got up and walked round to my side of the table, flicked my ear then kicked me really hard saying a flick and a kick for being so quick. Just you wait til next month Matthew. I now have a big bruise on my leg and at PE today sir asked me how I got it and I told him that I always get kicked at home on the first day of the month. Hopefully now Matthew will get arrested.

## Sunday 1st February
## Skip
Julia didn't fancy cooking today so we went for a curry at xxxxx. On the back of the door, down low so it's difficult to read, is a notice that says "Food Hygiene Rating 2 Stars". This is fantastic news as I would have thought most curry houses would have a nought. Mr xxxxx said that he has to display the notice but I told him that he should be proud of two stars. Apparently all food establishments are now not

just inspected but given a star rating. I wonder how many people it takes to inspect all the food establishments in the country? It all seems a bit pointless. Either somewhere's going to give you food poisoning or it's not. What about our own kitchens? Are we going to all have to put food hygiene ratings on our front doors? It would be quite good fun to invite people for dinner and then be told that so and so can't come because we only have a two star food hygiene rating! That would be one way to keep people away. What about at Christmas? There would be people up and down the country starving because they've turned up at Auntie Ruth's for Christmas to find that she only has two stars, despite the fact that she's been cooking for eighty years, makes the best Dundee cake in London, has a cat that sleeps on her work surface and has never poisoned anyone. Apparently two stars means "improvement necessary". Well, my chicken tandoori was excellent and if two stars means that I can always get a table then that's fine for me. I wonder what rating the Scout Hut would get? Not that Mr Scores on the Doors is going to get a chance to inspect our camp fire.

## Monday 2nd February
## Skip

Julia came home from work this evening with a huge, huge bagful of first aid stuff that the hospital was throwing out. It was stuffed full of plasters and bandages, enough to satisfy the first aid post of a World Jamboree for a hundred years. Apparently all first aid stuff has an expiry date on it and after that the hospital cannot use it. So what's going to happen when little Alex comes running to me with a nasty cut? I clean it, dry it and then, "Oh no! I'm sorry Alex but you're going to have to bleed to death because the sterile bandage and swab have gone past their expiry date." What nonsense. I'm not asking Alex to eat the bandage, am I? Mind you, it would be one way to shut him up. "Skip, I'm bleeding!" "Eat this!" Later on it would be, "Sorry, Alex's mum but Alex has bled to death, but he went very quietly, no noise at all, just a few muffled squawks." Still, at least we would get five stars from Mr Scores on the Doors for not serving out of date "food."

## Thursday 5th February
## Alex
Mummy had to go and see Miss Kayleigh after school today. (I hope she could understand what she was saying cos most of the time I can't like she's got a funny accent. She told us once that she came from a land down under which is just her being funny cos it's a song and doesn't really exist. She just can't speak properly). Mummy also had to see Mr Cameron. When mummy got home she said that Miss Kayleigh had said that she was concerned that I had been looking very tired at school recently. Mummy told me that she had told Miss Kayleigh that I was sleeping on the floor in a sleeping bag. Then she had to go and see Mr Cameron. Mr Cameron said that he was concerned about a large bruise on my leg. Mummy said that she didn't know anything about it. I didn't want to get Matthew into trouble so I said to mummy that I didn't know how it got there.

## Thursday 5th February
## Skip
Today I popped up to the Scout Hut to inspect our first aid kit. Some of the bandages in there are so old that they pre-date expiry dates. So that's okay then, we'll keep those for back-up and have a few of the expiry date ones in case of need. I wonder what happened before expiry dates - did

everyone who was bandaged with an old bandage then get gangrene and die? I also found a bottle in the kit of something called, "Spirit of Sal Volatile," with no expiry date. It says on the label that I should mix one teaspoonful to a half a glass of water. Then what, drink it? I opened the bottle and gave it a sniff and it stank! I've put it back for now, but I think that it's time for a new first aid kit. I'll order one in the morning.

## Friday 6th February
## Alex

Tonight was a big night! I am now officially a 3rd Chislehurst Scout. Skip had to explain that I was being invested after I got in a bit of a muddle with what was happening to me. He said that I was a one-off and that if I hadn't been conceived then I would certainly have had to have been invented. Now I know that I was being invested but now I have no idea what "conceived" means, only that I have been. I asked mummy this evening what "conceived" meant and she said, "thought of". Well, I've certainly been thought of. I wonder who's thought of me? Quite a few people probably. I had to make the Scout sign and say my Scout Promise. "On my honour, I promise to do my best, to do my duty to God (Chloe coughed) and to the Queen, to help other people and to keep the Scout Law". "And not to blow the bloody microwave doors off," added Matthew at the end and everyone giggled and Matthew was told off for swearing. He then told Skip that he was only quoting Michael Cane. Skip just said "misquoting" and carried on. Apart from that it was all perfect. I went second. Joe was invented as well. He was a Cub somewhere else but moved to 3rd Chislehurst because his mummy had been told we were nicer. Although I don't expect he thinks that now. He was invented first. He wasn't allowed to make a Jedi promise cos Skip said agaaaaain! that there wasn't one and that it was just an April Fool on the internet. Joe was very nervous, probably because he hadn't learnt his Scout Promise although he told me afterwards that he had learnt it, but had forgotten it. I don't think so! Joe is now in Eagle Petrol. I should have been an Eagle and he should have been a Woodpecker. Anyway, I'm going to get my Kestrel badge tomorrow. Joe's dad is a mechanic, which didn't help. When Joe started his Promise he said, "On my Honda, I Promise..." Skip stopped him and said that the word was "honour". Joe tried to pretend that that was what he said, but it wasn't, we all heard him. Then he said that he was making the "Mechanic's Promise" and Skip said, "Whatever". I got my Woodpecker badge and my 3rd Chislehurst badge and my membership badge and my moving on up badge and my district badge and my county badge and a new wobble. Mummy's going to be busy!

## Friday 6th February
## Skip
Investitures tonight and what a shambles. The Promise was all over the place. Chloe coughing (again), Jedis, Mechanics and Microwaves all making an appearance. To top it all, Joe wanted to make the Hindu Promise because I told him the Jedi one didn't exist. When I told him that he wasn't a Hindu he said that Chloe wasn't a Christian but she made the Christian Promise. So I said that he could make the Hindu Promise if he knew it, but he didn't so he made the normal one, eventually. Thank goodness for Alex who was word perfect although he added "Amen" at the end, explaining that at school everything with God in it ends with "Amen." I did explain he was making a Promise and not

43

saying a prayer. "I'm the one praying that you will do your best," I told him. Mind you, if this is what doing their best is, goodness knows what doing their worst is like.

When I got home I found an email from the "sticking our nose into your hygiene" rating people. How do they know about us? They want to come and do an inspection at the Scout Hut. This is going to be interesting, rating a camp fire and sticks that have been stripped of bark, sharpened and then stuck through a sausage. We have to be rated on three things: 1. "How hygienically the food is handled – how it is prepared, cooked, re-heated, cooled and stored." That'll be a no stars (urgent improvement necessary) then. 2. "The condition of the structure of the buildings – the cleanliness, layout, lighting, ventilation and other facilities." "Layout?" That's going to be even more interesting. "Tell, me Mr Scout Leader, why do you have three floors?" "Because, Mr Inspector, this used to be a stables, with the horses on the ground floor, the hay on the top and the manure downstairs. But I'm sure it was always kept very clean." So we'll probably get a minus one star (imminent danger of poisoning) for that. 3. "How the business manages what it does to make sure food is safe and so that the officer can be confident standards will be maintained in the future." I don't even understand that one so it will be an unclassified star (customers are dying). I've emailed back to explain that we do occasional cooking on the camp fire with skewered sausages, so we'll just have to wait and see what happens.

## Saturday 7th February
## Alex
I've ordered my Kestrel badge online. I told mummy that I wanted to buy a badge and she said that she would use her

credit card. I told her that the badge was only 79p. Unfortunately the postage was £4.60 so it became quite expensive for one badge. Fortunately mummy didn't have her glasses on so couldn't see how much she was paying which was just as well. Still, it will be worth it, to be a Kestrel and not a Woodpecker. No one will notice.

## Saturday 7th February
### Skip
I've been in a bit of a rush today but still found a few minutes to order a new first aid kit for the Scout Hut. Akela will be pleased. She's normally the one to sort these sorts of things out. "Brownie points for Skip!" so to speak.

## Thursday 12th February
### Alex
Mummy had to go and see Mr Evan today. She's never had to go and see the headmaster before. He told mummy that she needn't be ashamed to ask for help. He told her that not everyone in Chislehurst was stinking rich. He said that there was a nice little charity in Bromley that supplied second-hand furniture for only a few pounds and that he had found mummy a bed for me and did she need one herself? I told mummy that it wasn't my fault and that she should have said that I had a bed already. She said that she told Mr Evan that that was very kind of him and that she would go and have a look at it. Anyway, from now on I have to have something soft under my sleeping bag so I don't keep waking up. I wonder what James puts under his sleeping bag? If he's climbing Mount Everest he's probably hanging from a hammock that's been nailed into the mountain. I wonder if mummy will let me nail a hammock into my bedroom wall? Or I could hang it from the ceiling.

45

James can't do that. There aren't any ceilings on Mount Everest. I have put my duvet on the floor and the sleeping bag on that. It should be much more comfortable.

This evening mummy had a visit from a man from So Shawl Services. These are people who want to make sure that you're okay and I think want to keep you warm. A very nice man called Gary wanted to see my bruise so I asked him which one cos I normally have loads. He wanted to see the big one on my leg so I showed him. But it's not so big now. Then he asked me how I got it so I told him it was a secret. Then mummy had to leave the room and then he said that if I ever thought I was in danger I should call Childline then he asked me again. He said that no one would get into trouble, he just needed to know in case I was in any danger. I said that I wasn't in danger yet but I would be when I was Chief Scout cos they do dangerous things. I asked Gary if he had ever met James Ketchell cos he's always in danger. He said that he hadn't but that even if he had he wouldn't be able to tell me. This seems a bit odd. Why would someone not tell you if they've met someone famous who's cycled up Mount Everest and swum round the world, or something like that?

Then Gary said that he was concerned that I was in danger from other people, not things, and he kept staring at me so I started to talk to Scottie Dog who was on the floor. I said that I was only in danger from Skip cos he was going to show us how to use an axe. Gary wanted to know who Skip was so I said that he was my Scout leader and he was really cool and he liked doing things with children like camping and stuff. Then Gary said that I would probably be using an axe on wood and not a person so I told him that Josh's dad was in prison cos he had done something to a person like

46

chop them up or saw them up, probably anyway. Anyway, once Gary had promised not to tell I said that I had the big bruise from Matthew cos it was on a pinch and a punch day. Gary said that it didn't look much like a pinch or a punch so I said sillllllly! Doesn't he know anything? I had to explain that cos I did pinch and a punch first on Matthew he then gave me a flick and a kick for being so quick. I also told him that it wouldn't happen next month as I had promised not to pinch or punch but I hadn't promised not to flick or kick so Matthew would have the bruise but I may still get a punch which will probably give me a bruise but not very big and he can come back next month to have a look if he really needed to. Anyway, Gary didn't say anything so I looked up and he wasn't there and mummy came in and said that he had left and would I like anything for tea. She then said that I could have anything I liked for tea. Anything? Yes, anything. Like as a special treat so I said that I would like a helicopter.

Mummy sewed all my badges on my new shirt this evening so I gave her a kiss when Matthew wasn't looking. I love my mummy and I told her and I thought that she was going to cry. I told her not to cry and she said that it was cos she had been peeling onions. This is a bit odd cos we had fish and mash and peas for tea. No onions in sight. I said that you can zap onions in the microwave to make them less likely to make your eyes water. She said that she knew that but that someone had blown the bloody doors off and then she did cry. I told her that it wasn't that important and that Michael Cane had blown up a whole van.

**Friday 13th February**
**Alex**
No Scouts tonight as it's half-term, although half-term does

47

not officially start until Monday. Maybe it's because of the date. I spent my Scout meeting time in my room preparing my bivi shelter for my sleeping bag. If Hugo's dad has one then I need one. Daddy said that the basic shelters were just large bin bags which people like James would put their sleeping bags into to keep themselves dry if they didn't have a tent. I don't know why James would go up Mount Everest without a tent, especially as he would be prepared but anyway I was already thinking about my bivi sleeping bag. I got a black bin bag from the under the stairs cupboard and put my sleeping bag in it. It was a bit of a squeeze but I managed it. I am now in it and it's fine.

## Friday 13th February
### Skip
I've had an email back from the "sticking our nose into your hygiene rating" people. Apparently, as food is less than 25% of our trade we are exempt. That's a relief. Now we can continue to poison everyone. Not that we trade anything, apart from insults. Ha, ha.

## Saturday 14th February
### Alex
I didn't sleep very well last night. Every time I rolled over in my sleep I woke up. The bivi bag made a rustling sound every time I moved. It was the same noise that the bin bags make when daddy puts the rubbish out on Wednesdays. I probably thought in my head whilst I was asleep that I was about to be thrown into the back of a bin lorry. I wonder what happens on camp when you're sleeping in a bivi bag? I wonder how the bin men realise not to throw you in the bin lorry when they come to get the rubbish from the camp sites? I wonder if a Scout has ever been thrown in the back

of a bin lorry? Still, he would probably be asleep so wouldn't know much about it, getting all squished and squashed about like someone's making industrial quantities of mince for Scout pie. Mummy said that I can't keep the duvet on the floor as it will get all messy and will have to keep being washed. Back to square one, almost. In the morning when I woke up and climbed out of my bivi bag I found that my sleeping bag was soaking wet but my pyjamas were dry so I hadn't wet myself unless I had managed to do it through my sleeping bag like by magic. I phoned Hugo and he said that it was the condescension from my body heat which can escape the sleeping bag but not the black bin bag so I've now put loads of little holes in it (the black bag not the sleeping bag) with my Swiss Army Knife so that the condescension can escape.

Today is Saint Valentine's Day when you give a card to your girlfriend. I don't have a girlfriend but I made a card for Tegan cos I thought she would like to get one. I drew a picture of a camp fire and me and her cooking sosages on sticks and inside I wrote To Tegan. Cos you are supposed to share everything with your girlfriend I put I will also share my sosage with you. From Alex. Mummy had to go past her house so she took it round there. When mummy got back she said that she had seen Tegan's daddy on the drive so she gave him the card and said it was for Tegan and from me.

### Saturday 14th February
### Skip
The first aid kit has arrived and to quote Victor Meldrew, "I don't believe it!" In my haste I've managed to have gone and ordered a first aid kit for pets. Now what's Akela going to say? "Cat-astrophe", "Purrfect" or "You can use it when the

Scouts feel ruff." Enough of this nonsense. Funnily enough, all of the stuff is what we need anyway. There are bandages, gauzes, wipes and tweezers – that sort of thing. I took the cardboard wrapper off that said, "First Aid Kit for Pets" and now no one will be the wiser. I've taken out the First Aid for Pets booklet and put in Emergency First Aid Made Easy. At first I thought that I could do without purchasing a new booklet but I don't think we really need one at the moment from World War II that deals with things such as treating gas casualties. The only other item that I've removed is something that calls itself an "Elizabethan Collar" which goes round a dog's head to stop it scratching a wound. I always thought they were called "pet lamp shades." I should have left it in because we could play a great catching game with it if we stuck it round a Scout's head, but I expect the first Scout to put it on would be called "Rover" for ever and a day, so maybe not. Just to ensure I've not missed anything I decided to order a small human first aid kit (that is to say a small first aid kit for humans, not a first aid kit for small humans). It calls itself, "First Aid Essentials for Adults," so that should do the trick.

**Sunday 15th February**
**Alex**
Mummy said that Tegan's mummy rang up in the morning while I was still asleep and said that if I go anywhere near Tegan with my sosage she'll chop it off. I hope Tegan got my card and not her mummy. I think I wrote Tegan on it. I definitely didn't put Tegan's mum that's for sure. She is quite nice though.

**Monday 16th February**
**Alex**

It's no good. The bivi bag has got to go. It's still getting condescension only now it's on the outside because of all the holes. I thought that I would patch them all up and spent a very busy Sunday morning with the Sellotape. At lunchtime mummy had a sweary moment when I told her because I had used up all the Sellotape. She asked me why I didn't just use a new bin bag as they only cost a few pee each when I had used up several pounds' worth of tape. She doesn't realise that I'm trying to save every penny. This will be very necessary when she gets her credit card bill. I haven't told her that my sleeping bag is also full of holes like a giant performerated tea bag cos I should've taken the sleeping bag out of the black sack before making the holes in it rather than just stabbing it on the floor.

## Tuesday 17th February
## Alex

My Kestrel badge arrived today. Unfortunately mummy had to sign for the parcel cos I was at school. Inside there was tons of bubble wrap and in the middle my badge. Unfortunate because mummy wondered aloud, "How much must all that have cost?" and I said "Five pounds, thirty nine," and mummy had another sweary moment and said, "For one badge?" and I said that at least it had arrived safely. And then she had another sweary moment. Two sweary moments = One sweary period. And we don't want many of those, do we diary?

After she had finished her sweary period she took the Woodpecker badge off my shirt and sewed the Kestrel badge on but not before she had had a little paddy moment. This is like a sweary moment only with just the shouty bits. She asked why the Scouts don't have a sweary sewing badge and

I told her that that was the sort of thing that the Guides do and she said that in that case I should be a Guide. I told her that I couldn't be a Guide because I was a boy and that all the mummies sew badges on for their Scout children. However she then tried to tell me that Joe's mummy doesn't and that she uses badge glue. I tried to calm her down by telling her that if she sent the online people the Woodpecker petrol badge that I didn't need then they may refund her the five pounds, thirty nine and treat it as a swap. She then asked me who else was in Kestrel petrol and I said "no one". It was then that she realised that I was basically in a petrol of one, i.e. me. I said that she was not to worry and that no one would look at which petrol badge I was wearing as Skip knew which petrol I was in and so wouldn't look and none of the other Scouts took any notice. Anyway, for my – mummy's – money, I – she – also have the answer to my sleeping bag / duvet problem. Bubble wrap!

**Friday 20th February**
**Alex**
The bubble wrap is working well as insulation and there is no condescension. However, whenever I roll over one or two bubbles pop and I wake up. I don't know how to stop myself rolling over so the bubble wrap will also have to go. When I saw Hugo today he said that his mummy refuses to sew any of his badges on and so he sticks them on with glue. Just like Joe's mum. That's a great idea! Joe's mum's a bit suspect but if Hugo's mum's doing it then it must be okay. I unpicked all the badges from my shirt and then stuck them all on with some of daddy's Pritt Stick. Mummy's sewing was fine but I won't be held to ransom every time she is asked by me to sew a badge on. And there are going to be many of those moments. So I shall do my own. My county

badge, my district badge, my membership badge, my 3rd Chislehurst name badge, my moving on up and finally my Kestrel badge. I wrote my name on the collar with a big red Sharpie so everyone knows it's my shirt when I go on camp and everything gets muddled up.

I made a tent today for my sleeping bag (with extra ventilation) to go in. And me, obviously. I couldn't use a real tent as I would have to put tent pegs in the floor and mummy wouldn't be very pleased if I did that so I used a large piece of plastic sheeting that I found in the garage that I draped over some string. I tied the string, using a clover hitch which is a knot that Skip has taught us as a secure start to all lashings. I tied my clover hitch to my wardrobe knob and was going to tie the other end to the door knob but then I thought that would be a bit silly because every time someone opens the bedroom door my tent will collapse so I've tied the other end to one of the chest of draws' handles. That worked cos no one's going to open the chest of draws while I'm in my tent. I then opened up the sheeting and put some books on each corner to hold it in place. The sleeping bag and duvet then went in and the bubble wrap stayed out.

## Saturday 21st February
## Skip

"I don't believe it – again!" Why is it that, when I order a first aid kit, I get a variation on a first aid kit? My "First Aid Essentials for Adults" has turned up. Now I know it wasn't very expensive but I thought something wasn't quite right when it came in a brown envelope with "Emergency Supplies" printed on the front. I opened up the envelope and found six-glow-in-the-dark condoms. Presumably they have to be charged up first so they wouldn't be much use in an emergency. I've had enough of this first aid kit lark. I'll put them in the pets' first aid kit. It'll give Akela a giggle when she goes on the Cub camp that's coming up. In the meantime, I think I need a sniff or slurp of that "Spirit of Sal Volatile," whatever it is.

## Saturday 21st February
**Alex**

My first night in my new tent has gone really well. Mummy said that I was stupid tying the string to the wardrobe and chest of draws as each time I opened them my tent would collapse. Then she added, not very helpfully, "Not that they get opened very often." I told her that it would only be a problem if wardrobe and drawer were opened at the same time as then I would suffocate and she wouldn't be able to open them both at the same time as she can't reach both at the same time unless she's Captain Elastic which she's not. Anyway, my tent has stayed and my Woodpecker badge is going. I won't get £5.49 for it though.

## Sunday 22nd February
**Alex**

I had to hide in the garden today cos mummy was cleaning my room and found loads of little holes in the carpet. I told her that at least the floorboards won't get condescension and mummy had a paddy and said that she was could kill me and she was smiling as she said it. So I took the phone outside and rang Childline like Gary said and I told the lady that my life was in danger cos my mummy had said that she was going to kill me. The lady said that she would phone the police and I was to hide until they arrived. I went to hide in daddy's shed but I found daddy in there and he was doing "potting up" with little plants and so I told him that I was

54

hiding from mummy cos she was going to kill me and that I had phoned Childline and they had phoned the police. Daddy didn't seem bothered cos I don't suppose mummy's going to kill him then we heard nar-nah, nar-nah and daddy said that I should go and tell the policeman that I was still alive. When I got round the front mummy was in hand-cuffs round her wrists and a nice lady policeman said was I okay and I said yes and I asked her if she knew Josh's dad cos he's in prison but she didn't. Mummy then had to explain that she was only going to kill me metaforikely or something like that. I think it means a little bit. After quite a long time mummy was de-arrested and allowed to go back indoors. Then the policeman lady asked me if I had any other adults looking after me so I said that I had daddy but he didn't look after me very well. I think I meant to say not very much but I was a little bit scared. Then she asked me where he was so I said that he was in his shed with his pot. Then she told me to go indoors and all the policemen and there were loads of them went down the side of the house and then they went away. When daddy came in the back door I was sitting at the table having a hot chocolate but it was the special hot chocolate. Mummy said that I could have anything (but not a helicopter). I said I wanted a hot choc. I was allowed the special hot choc. which is the Fortnum and Masons' March mallow hot chocolate which actually has little March mallows on top and then mummy put more March mallows on top but the ones on top are from Tescos so they're not as nice. Daddy said that the policemen had asked him what he was growing and he said McDreamy and Mr Stripey and when they asked him if they were some kind of narcotic he said no, they were sweary tomato plants. Then they left.

**Friday 27th February**

## Alex

Scouts is back, thank goodness. With all my new badges glued on I looked very smart with my new shirt and ironed scarf, which I did myself. Skip decided to have a badge inspection. This was something that we never had in Cubs and until today I never knew even existed. I wish Akela had warned me. Skip explained that he didn't give badges out to Scouts who didn't get them sewn on so was going to check to make sure that we were all "up to date". I passed with flying colours although Skip said that my badges were a bit "skew-whiff". I wanted to tell him that it wasn't easy gluing badges but I didn't want him to know so I kept quiet. Skip didn't even notice my Kestrel, he put me in front of all the other Scouts and then said to Josh that if he, i.e. Josh, wasn't a little more "handy" with his badge-sewing he may find that I, i.e. yours truly, would become assistant patrol leader before he, Josh, had been reinstated. Josh then said that at least he had the correct badges, even if they were still in his pocket. The cat was out of the bag. When mummy collected me Skip told her that I needed to swap the Kestrel over with the Woodpecker. That means I have a problem as yesterday I swapped my Woodpecker badge with Nico for three Haribos. It's just as well that mummy's gone out now otherwise she would have made me start looking for a Woodpecker badge that I knew that I wouldn't find cos Nico has it and I've eaten the Haribos so can't swap back.

Next week we're going on camp. This time it's a proper camp which means it's not near the Scout Hut. It's going to be a survival camp as the district camp for the Outdoors Challenge Award has been cancelled as the Scout leader who was arranging it has broken both his wrists. I wonder how he did that? He was probably mucking about and not being

56

prepared. Maybe he was in handcuffs and they were put on too hard. I don't expect James has ever broken his wrists. Not both at the same time anyway. I wonder how he has a shower with two broken wrists? He can't get them wet cos the bandages are plaster so it would melt. I wonder how he holds the soap or maybe he has it dangling down from the ceiling on a bit of string and then has to sort of bump into it. Well I hope I'm going to survive survival camp. I don't want to die on my first proper camp. I don't even want to break my wrists. Skip has given mummy a form to sign and us Scouts a check list of stuff we need to bring. We never used to get a check list in Cubs. I expect Akela gave the list to the parents or maybe not cos I always had loads of stuff missing. Josh said that when he was in Cubs he was on a district camp and he unpacked his rucksack and at the bottom there was a envelope with TOP MAN! written on it in scribbly writing and when he opened it there was a thousand pounds in it! So I asked him what he did with it and he said that he bought every person on the camp an ice cream and there were hundreds of people. I said that it was probably his daddy's money and why didn't he tell him when he got home but he said that his daddy was away. I think he's away for a very long time so when he comes back a thousand pounds won't be worth very much what with infellation and things like that so he might as well've bought ice creams. Cor, can you imagine if Josh went on camp and said ice creams all round and I was the only person around? I could have an ice cream every day for years! Never mind. We must put all our kit in a rucksack but I can't find mine now but I do still have the black sack with holes (patched up) so I can use that. That will save mummy a load of money so she'll be pleased with me.

## Friday 27th February
## Skip

I decided to have a badge inspection to ensure that all the badges that I had given out had been sewn on. Tegan didn't have a scarf, Trudy had a shirt and scarf but no woggle and Sarah-Jane had a scarf and woggle but no shirt. Josh had all his badges in his pocket. Nico had a load of Alpe d'Huez badges. I told him that they weren't Scout badges but he said that he had been skiing for half-term and bought them because he liked them and he had nowhere else to put them. "Badge blanket?" Apparently he doesn't own one as his mother won't allow him to go camping. For some reason Alex had "Alex" written on his shirt collar so I asked him why. He told me it was so that on camp everyone would know it was his. When I told him that he should have put it under the collar he said that no one would look under there. "What about the label that has a space for 'name'?" Alex said that his Sharpie was a bit thick and so there was only space for an "A" and that wasn't much use as it could mean "Abi" or "Adult". His badges were immaculate though, if a little lop-sided, until Josh blurted out that Alex had the wrong patrol badge. So then I had to tell his mother at pick-up that he needed to have the Woodpecker badge that I had given him sewn on. Then she's decides to tell me that she can't see what the problem is because, "They're all birds, aren't they?" I did try to explain the patrol system and that Alex wasn't in Kestrels, so she suggested that I move him into Kestrels as that would be easier. "We don't have a Kestrel patrol," I explained patiently. "You do now, Skippy," she said with a cackle.

The Outdoor Challenge Award camp has now been cancelled as Dick has broken both wrists in a zip-wire accident. Dick indeed. Apparently both arms are bandaged from shoulder to wrist. He hadn't installed a breaking mechanism so when the zip wire came to a sudden halt at the end, Dick was thrown off and was doing a superman impersonation but pointing downwards. He therefore used his wrists as brakes. Effective but painful. I suppose that's one way to use up loads of excess bandages. I hope they were all in-date.

Scouts have been given kit lists for the alternative camp. The trouble is, no one reads them so I've added "One bottle of whiskey" for a laugh. In fact, the Scouts should know what to bring so I've redone the whole kit list. The suggested one reads:

## Nights Away Kit List
All young people will need to bring their personal equipment and should be encouraged to pack themselves. This list is only a guide.
Complete uniform
Warm sweaters, jumpers or sweatshirts
T-shirts or similar
Trousers or shorts
Spare underclothes (one pair per day)
Spare socks (one pair per day)
Nightwear
Hike boots or strong shoes; wellies
Waterproof (coat and trousers)
Swimwear and towel
Hankies
Personal washing requirements and towel
Scarf, hat and gloves
Sun hat, sun cream and sun glasses

Sleeping bag
Foam roll / Karrimat
Plate, bowl, mug and cutlery
Tea towel
Torch and spare batteries
Personal first aid kit
Towel (Large)
Day sack and plastic drinks bottle
Polythene bags (for dirty clothes)
Teddy!
Games
A small packet of individually wrapped sweets (to be handed in on arrival)
It is best to pack a rucksack or sports bag that you can carry on your back. Suitcases are not suitable for tents.
Medication should be clearly marked with name of young person and dosage and handed in on arrival.
All items should be clearly labelled with the young person's name.

My new one reads:

### Not-Nights Away Kit List
All young people will need to bring their personal equipment but should never, under any circumstances, pack themselves. Parents must ensure that they come and repack for their young people, before returning home. Five items each must always be left at the campsite. This list is definitive and must be adhered to.
Complete uniform (less woggle, scarf and shirt)
Warm sweaters for daytime
T-shirt (One only)
Jeans (for water activities or when raining)

Spare underclothes (One pair per week)
Spare sock
Nightwear (Onesies only)
Footwear (Flip-flops, or wellies that are two sizes too small, for the hikes)
Black sack with three extra holes for head and arms in case of wet weather
Swimwear not required for water activities as the lake is not overlooked
Hankies (Preferably used)
Wash Bag (Empty)
Scarf, hat and gloves (for hot weather)
Sun hat, sun cream and sun glasses (for indoor or evening activities)
Sleeping bag (for keeping dirty clothes in)
Polythene bags (for sleeping in)
Foam (Shaving not roll)
Plate, bowl, mug (One item only)
Cutlery (One item only)
Tea towel (New)
Torch or glow-stick (No batteries allowed, spare batteries strictly forbidden)
Personal first aid kit (Two items maximum, no plasters)
Towel (Flannel-size best, especially for swimming)
Day sack (Carrier bag preferable)
Whisky (For leaders but young people can look after it if preferred)
iPad, iPhone, iPod (All three)
Pack of cards (with no lid)
A large packet of loose sweets or cake to be kept in the tent, preferably scattered around, to ensure that you're not lonely at night. You will quickly make friends with not only your fellow humans, but also all the friendly wildlife from ants

and bugs to foxes and badgers.

It is best to pack a large suitcase and leave it outside the tent at all times, preferably open.

The suitcase should have a hidden compartment for parents to include all the items that were missed off the kit list.

Medication must also be put in said hidden compartment.

Under no circumstances must any item bear the young person's name. This is for safeguarding reasons.

Gosh, I hope they don't take things too literally. I did emphasise to them though, that they must make sure that they bring their sleeping bags and torches – the two most essential items of any kit list.

## Saturday 28th February
### Alex

Mummy asked me at breakfast where my Woodpecker badge was and I said that I didn't know, which is true. After breakfast I went online and was more than overjoyed, overjoyed plus you could say as I'm a Scout, to find that the badge shop that I had bought my Kestrel badge from also sells Woodpecker badges. So I put one in the shopping basket and when I clicked to pay the computer asked if I wanted to use the same credit card as I, aka mummy, had used before. I just clicked "Yes" and the order was accepted. I clicked on the "next day delivery" button as I wanted the badge to arrive before mummy started shouting. This is fantastic news. My life has been saved and I haven't even had to bother mummy. £5.39 is a small price to pay for my life to be saved. I'll tell mummy that if she has a little moment.

## Sunday 1st March

## Alex

A bad day, then a good day. A bad day first. I got up early and went into Matthew's room where he was asleep. I put a little chair by his bed and stood on it. Then I kicked him as hard as I could and whispered no flick but a kick for being a dick. Then he screamed and I told him to shhsh but he wouldn't he kept screaming then daddy came in and turned on the light and said what's going on and I said that I had kicked Matthew cos I wasn't allowed to pinch or punch him and daddy pulled Matthew's duvet off him and how was I to know that he was sleeping the wrong way round and I had kicked him in the head and so daddy smacked me and so I said that I was going to call Childline again and daddy disappeared and came back with the phone and said go on then cos if I do I'll be taken into care and mummy and daddy would get their lives back. Then Matthew said that when I had finished he wanted the phone so that he could phone Childline and report me. Then we all went back to bed and no one said anything more about it. When Matthew came down to breakfast he forgot to pinch and punch me and I wasn't going to tell him. He did have a HUGE black eye though. I hope Gary doesn't see it.

After that it was a good day! Mummy and daddy took me to Cotswold Outdoor in the Nugent Centre to get a rucksack. The Nugent Centre is near the River Cray which is very smelly but they have some nice shops there although it's normally very difficult to park so mummy (and daddy) get very sweary and mummy has to go to M and S to buy something and daddy has to go to the pub but the local pub is now a McDonalds which is even worse than drinking so he doesn't go there but there's no pub in the Nugent Centre so he has to go into Nandos but then he has to get a meal as well which makes one beer quite expensive. They bought me a Vango. Just in time! And it's C of E approved. It has loads of pockets and straps and loops that I don't know what to do with as there are no instructions. It's called a "60 + 10" which is the number of litres that it holds, not that I'm going to fill it with water to find out. Why they can't just call it a "70" I don't know. Maybe they think we need a maths lesson as well cos this rucksack's only for clever people. Like, what's 60 + 10? Er, 80? No, I'm sorry you can't have that rucksack, you'll have to have a cheaper one or a smaller one. I bet daddy would have said 80 to get out of paying for one but no one asked so I got it. When we got home, despite being a Sunday when everyone's out at church or shopping, a parcel arrived for mummy, even though it's not her birthday. It had to be "signed for" so Daddy said that it must be quite important. He opened it whilst mummy was in the garden, thank goodness, and inside loads more bubble wrap was my precious new Woodpecker badge. Daddy didn't say anything, he just gave it to me and went back to his newspaper. When mummy came in daddy went out to his shed which was also a thank goodness. I gave mummy the badge and when she asked where I had found it I said that I hadn't and that daddy had given it to me, which wasn't a lie. At dinner time, mummy asked daddy where he had found the Woodpecker badge and he just said, "Underneath loads of bubble wrap." Phew, mummy didn't ask any more questions. She probably assumed that daddy had looked under the other bubble wrap in my bedroom under my bed. Why she would think that daddy would be under the bubble wrap under my bed, I've no idea. Maybe she just thought he was being thorough. Anyway, every cloud has a silver lining, and I now have even more bubble wrap although I don't know what I'm going to do with it so that's gone under the bed as well. At least Scottie Dog's warm.

In the afternoon we had to go to the Scout Hut with our mummies and daddies for a camp briefing. We have a new assistant Scout leader. It's Laura's dad and he's really cool. Mind you, Laura's really cool. She's not like a girl at all and that's why she will make a good Scout. In Scouts we call our leaders after ship people, so we have Skip(per) to start with. Trudy's dad is called Crusher. Tegan's dad is called Gunner but he only comes on camp. We don't see him at any other time. Yvonne's dad helps sometimes and he's called Bomber which isn't very ship-like but he wanted to be called it and that was that. Skip asked us what we would like to call Laura's dad and he read out a list of obvious ones like Captain or Admiral. No one liked these and so they were rejected. Skip then said that he was moving on to his b-list which I think stands for bloody-list because none of us could make a decision. He read out some really odd names and we all decided that Laura's dad should be called Jimmy the One. This is a nickname for the First Left Tenant of a ship, otherwise known as Jimmy. This was fine all afternoon until Laura's mum came to pick them both up and we all said "goodbye, Jimmy." Skip then had to explain to the parents that it was Laura's dad's new navy name and that they should be relieved because he could have been called "Buffer" or "Pussy" which made them all laugh, although I don't know why. One sounds like something you get at Charing Cross Station and the other a kitten, both of which have no place on a ship, at least not 3rd Chislehurst's ship. Skip's told the parents that Crusher, Gunner and Jimmy are all assholes. Bomber isn't. This means that Bomber isn't allowed to wear a Scout leaders' shirt.

My first proper Scout camp next week. Skip has told us to look at our kit lists closely and not to forget our sleeping bags and tortures. I've had a look at the list and can't see anything about tortures. Maybe he doesn't want the parents to know what we're up to. The sleeping bag I do have (holey) but I don't have any tortures. I hope that no one's going to hurt me although it is all about survival. I went down to daddy's shed this evening and found a Big Nipper Rat Trap. It has "EXTRA POWER" stamped on it. This will make a great torture. You pull back a metal bar on a spring and then hold it in place with another metal bit and wait for a rat to walk on the platform. Then, no torture, but instant death! Still, it will have to do.

I've looked through the rest of the kit list and it all looks very sensible. However, there's one thing that really worries me. There's no way mummy is going to pack my rucksack. I'm going to do it all by myself. I bet James doesn't get his mummy to pack his kit when he's climbing up Mount Everest or swimming round the world. Mind you, you wouldn't need much kit if all you're doing is swimming. Maybe just a pair of swimming trunks or a pair of jeans to keep you warm when you're swimming at night. I suppose you could get away with wearing nothing if you're swimming, especially at night, although you wouldn't want to get your nodger nibbled halfway across the Atlantic Ocean. You'd need some bandages then, out of date or not out of date.

I've asked daddy for some whisky for camp and he's given me a bottle to give to Skip. I don't think that I want to give it to Skip though cos it's really old and therefore will be very out of date although there's not an out of date stamp on it.

Why can't daddy give him a new bottle instead of one that says it's 15 years old? I know what I'll do, I'll scribble the 5 out with my black Sharpie so that is says Aged 1 Years which will be much better.

## Sunday 1st March
### Skip
Two of my ASLs have signed up for the camp, Crusher and Gunner. All the forms have been filled in and emailed off. It really is becoming quite depressing, this nickname lark. I now have Crusher, Gunner, Bomber and Jimmy the One. They're starting to sound less like ship's crew and more like a team of safe blowers.

## Friday 6th March
### Alex
My first proper camp as a Scout! I'm at xxxxx camp site near Biggin Hill. "Home of the Spitfire," said Gunner. Well, he would know. Tegan said that her dad is forty so he was probably in the war. Anyway, I could have worked that out for myself without being told that he was at least forty as only men over forty wear rock star t-shirts. Then Gunner added, "The 'plane, not the drink." Whoever would call a drink "Spitfire?"

We were all put in two-man or four-man tents although I'm glad I'm not a man otherwise it would have been a bit of a squeeze. The tent people must use midgets for working out how many would fit in their tents. I'm sharing a two-man tent with Joe although he's hardly a man. I wonder why they are Man tents and not Woman tents? What would the difference be? I expect the Woman tents would be a different colour inside and they could have mirrors and stuff. It's a bit odd sharing a tent with Joe, especially as he doesn't understand hygiene. One of the things we had to do this evening was find out why personal and campsite hygiene is important and what we should do to be hygienic. Joe reckons that to be hygienic we need to look as though we are clean. This means to him that when, as he did earlier on, you get a bit muddy putting the tent up, you have to cover up all your muddy clothes with clean ones, otherwise, "it means taking them all off," which Joe reckons is a bit of a faff. He's now in his sleeping bag wearing nearly all the clothes that he's brought for the weekend. He may be hygienic now, but by Sunday he's going to pong a bit. I put the Big Nipper in Barnaby's sleeping bag during supper and hot choc. He won't mind being tortured.

Joe has a great big bar of chocolate which he found in his wash bag. He said that his mummy always puts a bar in there to check if he's used his wash stuff, but all he does is takes the chocolate out and leaves the wash-stuff in although he says he always squeezes some toothpaste out onto the ground and rubs a bit of the soap off to make it look used.

Joe unpacked his rucksack, which meant just tipping everything out. "Ah," he said. "This is insect repellent that mum gave me so we won't get bitten tonight." It was called Trek 100 and it says on the container that it's for, "extreme tropical conditions such as jungle terrain, protecting travellers from insect-borne diseases such as malaria, dengue fever and West Nile virus." I don't think that we're likely to get malaria in [camp site] but I guess you never know. Joe then sprayed the whole of the inside of the tent with it and it stank. I told him that I thought we were

68

supposed to spray ourselves with it like our hands and feet and exposed bits but Joe said that it would work better on the tent walls and ceiling cos the insects would smell it from the outside and not come in.

I unpacked my rucksack (carefully) and at the bottom I found the bottle of whisky. I showed Joe and he got out his crockery bag and so I gave him a plastic mugful of it. Joe has brought a plate and a bowl and a mug which wasn't allowed. I've only brought a plate. I haven't had any whisky cos I think it's meant for Skip. I think we're allowed to look after it but I don't think that we're supposed to drink it. I was going to drink some but I only have a plate so I poured some on my plate but it was very difficult to keep it on the plate and it all slopped off and onto my sleeping bag and now it smells. The smell isn't too bad though. It's like the smell that I get when I go to daddy's shed. I'll give Skip the rest of it.

When I arrived this evening I showed Skip my new rucksack with Scottie Dog sticking out of the top and told him that it was C of E approved and he said, "Thank God!" and chuckled which was a bit rude. So I ignored him.

## Friday 6th March
### Skip
Nico has decided to come camping! This is a first. I'm all for encouraging the young people to get out more but I thought that if Nico came, I would probably get his mother as well, holding a wet flannel. I wasn't far wrong. No sooner had I arrived on camp to set up than the texts started. The first one was, surprise, surprise, from Nico's mum, "Nico's really looking forward to camp – he has enough stuff for a three week holiday! NO idea how he's going to carry it all!? I've

sent him along with twelve hot chocolate sachets. Please keep him away from the vending machines!!! Look after my baby! Sue. xxxxx" What are these mothers like?! I've sent her a reply. "We have hot chocolate. I have a two kilo tin which should suffice. He has been allocated one quarter of a four-man Scout tent as it will be full of four Scouts, or one half of a two-man Scout tent as it will be full of two Scouts. He doesn't need to be kept away from the vending machine if you don't give him any money."

Then I got, "Oh, no! I gave him £20 for emergencies. Can he have an extra tent for his stuff, or can he keep it in the mess tent or in your car?" Replied, "No, he will have his kit photographed and a parent named and shamed on Facebook. There will be no emergencies requiring money. We have food, we have first aid, we have hospitals free at the point of delivery. There is nothing for him to spend his money on." I thought that that would do the trick, but no. Five minutes later, "Beep, beep, beep," and this text appeared, "Oh, no! Pauline is already bringing him along with xxxxx and xxxxx. Sounds like they both have the same amount each also. (Kit and money). Let's see how many kits she can get photographed with! LOL! Don't be too hard on Nico as he's used to staying 5 star and with me packing you're lucky he hasn't got a dozen pairs of shoes. Still, he should be warm!" Replied, "How warm?" "Oh, well I couldn't get a 4-season bag like you suggested so I've got him three and put one inside the other inside the other." "And how will Nico fit into three sleeping bags?" "Don't ask me, I'm not the Scout leader."

Five minutes later and it was Josh's mother: "Josh has a weak bladder, so he may wet himself in the night before he gets to the toilet. Don't tell anyone though." "It's okay, I'll give him a Lucozade bottle but it would have been useful if you had put his condition on the health form." I didn't have a Lucozade bottle to hand so I gave him a fizzy water one when I saw him later in the evening. It should suffice. "A present from your mother," I told him. He just looked puzzled so I told him, "Fill it up if you need to, with whatever you want to fill it up with."

Finally, I received a text one from Tegan's mother. It asked simply, "Have you seen my mirror?" I had no idea what she was talking about so I just replied, "No."

Gunner's wearing his favourite t-shirt. He told me that he saw Mullit in Val d'Isere when he was skiing there at half-term a few years ago. "The best rock and roll band in the Alps," was his take on the group. All the Scouts were looking at it with its distinctive design. I bet they think Gunner's really trendy, wearing such a cool shirt. Puts my i-Scout shirt to shame.

Gunner's little daughter has come to stay on camp as well as Tegan. She's only six. This evening I was sitting in the mess tent with her and Gunner when Gunner suddenly asked, "Can you look after Teresa for a few minutes?" and then just walked off without waiting for an answer. As six-year olds aren't really my target age-range for Scouting I decided to play it safe with what we could talk about during Gunner's absence. "Let's ask each other some questions," I said to her as I popped her down on the Tilley lamp box and kneeled down beside her. "What's your favourite colour?" I asked. "Hmmmmm." She put her finger to her lips and looked up at the roof of the tent. No reply was forthcoming so after a minute or so of waiting I tried a little encouragement. "It's not supposed to be a difficult question. I just thought that you might have a favourite colour." After another minute and a couple more "hmmmms" the verbal floodgates opened. She had obviously been considering at length. "I suppose I quite like pink. But I also like red. Then I did like purple once. I don't like black, or orange or green and I don't really like yellow unless it's the sun... Blue." Well, thank goodness that was sorted. "Blue eh? Like the sky?" I wasn't expecting an answer but she said, "No, not really, not sky blue. Sometimes sky blue when it gets darker. But not when it's red cos then it's not blue. I like blue like glaucous. "'Glaucous'? What's that?" "It's a blue, silly. It's a blue powder colour that you get on grapes." "You're very clever aren't you?" Teresa just smiled then "tee-heed." "Would you like to be a Scout? I could do with some brains about the place." Teresa shook her head. "Very wise. Now you ask me a question." "What's six times ten?" "Sixty," I replied without having to hmmmm. Teresa didn't say anything. She just sat there on the box and smiled a toothless smile. I asked her, "Is that correct?" "I don't know," she said, "That's why I asked you." It was going to be a long few minutes.

No one's mentioned the kit list at all. No one's given me a bottle of whisky. Everyone seems to have brought all their kit and everything is sorted. I don't know why we bother with kit lists. Everyone knows what to bring and what not to bring.

It's quite a warm evening, considering. As we're sitting round a small camp fire with not a glass of whisky in our hands and whilst I'm writing up my diary, the girl's tent on the other side of the field looks as though they're having a disco inside with lights flashing on and off against the canvas walls and roof. I'll have to go and investigate. Maybe today's diary entry has a little further to go...

There is a saying amongst Scout leaders that, "You think you've seen it all, and then..." And now I know why. I crept up to the girls' tent and there was chatting and giggling - nothing unusual. Then I heard the dulcet tones of Agnetha and Anna-Frid singing "Dancing Queen, young and sweet only seventeen..." complete with strobe lighting. "Girls," I called through the door, "do you have Abba in there with you?" The strobing stopped and all went dark and quiet. "Not exactly, Skip." "I didn't mean exactly. Who has their phone?" "It's not a phone Skip, it's an iPod." "I've banned them. Who's is it?" "Lucy-Jane's." Now it's not too often that one has to tell one's own daughter off, but favouritism is banned during camp, so she was certainly going to get a telling off. Mainly because she doesn't own an iPod. "Who's iPod is it, Lucy-Jane?" I asked through the canvas. "Mummy's." "Does she know that you have it?" "Er, no." And then, as if to assuage her guilt she added, "Tegan's stolen her mum's mirror." Now the evening was getting interesting. There was something about this magic mirror for firstly Tegan's mother to text me about and now for Lucy-Jane to inform about. "What's so special about this mirror?" Cue plenty of giggling, as, as if by magic, Abba's next track from the iPod suddenly came on and wafted gently through the canvas. It was, "Does your Mother Know?" appropriately enough. "We're using it as a disco light." "Well how big is this mirror?" I asked, expecting them to say, "About the size of a phone" or something similar. Instead, Lucy-Jane said, "As tall as Tegan," to which Trudy added, "And as wide." This I had to see. "Are you all

73

decent?" I asked. "Well, we're all onesied up, Skip, as usual. Y'know like cows, pink rabbits, that sort of thing. Oh, and Laura's a hippo." "Yes, yes, okay. I don't need to be told that there's a farmyard and a zoo in there. Let me see this mirror." And with that the door was untied and the mirror came forth. It was about four feet high and a foot across. It was in a plain wooden frame with screw holes in each corner and halfway up each side. "Good gracious, Tegan," I said, "Where did you get that from?" "Her mum's wardrobe," said Trudy, who was holding onto it, without giving Tegan the chance to respond. "Well, no wonder your mother was looking for it!" I said. "She's obviously gone to look in it and found that it's missing." "I didn't think she would notice," said Tegan feebly from somewhere inside the darkness of the tent. "We never have a mirror big enough on camp. I've only borrowed it." "Yeah, and then I found if you flash your torch at it you can make like a big disco ball," said Trudy. "So how's your mum going to get dressed tomorrow when she goes out for the evening, with no bedroom mirror?" "Well, she'll just end up looking like I normally do on camp, Skip," said Tegan with a giggle. I thought that that was where this little episode was going to end. In fact, this was just the beginning. I felt a bit like the GP who deals with a patient's very minor complaint and then, as the patient reaches the surgery door, turns round and says quietly, "There is just one other thing doctor..." I started to tie the door up from the outside. This is an effort in itself. Had the girls agreed to have the smaller polypropylene tents it would have been, "zip, zip, job done." But no, the girls – all five of them (Chloe was fast asleep) – needed an eight man (woman) canvas patrol tent. They had plenty of space, that's for sure, even with a wardrobe mirror.

"Okay, girls," I said gently. "You'd better be getting off to sleep. But there's nothing else in there that I should know about is there? Girls? Girls?" It had fallen very quiet, for a second time. "Please, Skip," said Trudy, "there is something in here that you should know about" "Yes, Trudy?" I asked quietly. Now I was getting a little nervous. A Scout that says "please" when they're not asking for anything other than a little understanding can often be a cause for concern. I was at least relieved that she said "something" and not "someone." As far as I was aware all the boys were accounted for. "Please Skip, Laura has a chicken." A WHAT?! I remained very calm. "A chicken?" I asked composedly. "Yes," she whimpered. "Hopefully a frozen one?" My initial thought was that it was for Saturday's dinner that they were going to be preparing and that they had cheated by bringing extra meat. Then I thought that that wasn't going to work, bringing a chicken for the camp fire, as Laura's a vegetarian." "No, Skip. A real, live chicken. It's in the corner. It's a cockerel. Please don't be cross, but you need to know. It's getting a bit smelly" "Okay, bring him out," I sighed. Once more the tent door was untied and Laura appeared, looking as if she had been crying. In her arms was indeed a cockerel, the most enormous Rhode Island Red I had ever seen. "Laura?" "Buck, buck, buck, buckAHHHH!" crowed the cockerel. "I know you say 'no boys in the tent'" she said with a sniff, "but I think Isambard is different." "Different indeed," I said. "Bring him into the mess tent and let's have a chat."

Laura walked over to the mess tent with me leading the way, as I called to Gunner and Crusher to "come and have a look at this." I opened up the mess tent flap and announced to the lads, who were coming in from the other end, that we had found a boy in the girl's tent. With that Isambard made his entrance, still held tightly under Laura's arm. "You can put him down in here, Laura. Now sit down and tell us what's going on." I wanted to ask her more than "what's going on?" I wanted to ask "Who," "What," Why," When," "Where" and "How?" I wanted to ask, "What on earth do you think you're doing bringing a CHICKEN on camp?" but there comes a time on all camps, especially late in the evening and during an emergency (and it's more often than not the case that on camp emergencies tend to happen late in the evening) that questions become superfluous because, whatever the answers are, it's not going to resolve the emergency. Not that Isambard was really an emergency. "It's dad," cried Laura. "We've always had chickens but no one's complained before. Now Mrs xxxxx who lives next door has complained to the Council that Isambard is waking her up at six o'clock in the morning and the Council have written to dad and told him that we can't keep him cos he's a noise nuisance and dad's not on camp so I think I know why and I know that if I didn't bring Isambard on camp I would go back and find him gone." "Or eaten," added Crusher, somewhat unsympathetically. "Well, he's not gone and he's not eaten. He's here and he's safe. His breed is the state bird of Rhode Island in America and we should respect that. We'll look after him, Laura. And you need to go back to bed. We'll sort out what to do with him in the morning."

It does all seem a bit crazy. He's only made a couple of "BuckAHHH!"s so far and now is fast asleep. Doesn't Mrs xxxxx know that Chislehurst is effectively countryside, despite being referred to in Wiki as "affluent suburban district"?

76

## Saturday 7th March
## Afternoon
## Alex

I had a funny dream last night that one of the boys was in the girls' tent and the girls were calling him Isambard. It must have been a dream cos we don't have any Scouts or leaders called Isambard. He didn't speak properly either. He just made funny, cackling sounds. Could've been Josh I suppose. I woke up quite early cos all the birds were making a real racket. It's called a dawn chorus but it starts in the middle of the night and keeps going till you've woken up then it stops. It's a bit like a bird alarm clock only it goes off a bit too early, even when it's a school day.

I've been bitten a few times, so has Joe. So that's a "no-no" to spraying the tent with insect repellent. I don't expect the tent got bitten though.

Joe started to pong this morning. He woke up all sweaty and was really smelly. It was so bad that one of the other Scouts had wrapped toilet paper all round our tent as if to make a point or cover up the smell. Well thanks! Cos I was inside this toilet. I told Joe to go and have shower but he couldn't get his clothes off as they were so muddy they had dried and stuck to him. So he went and had a shower with his clothes on and then got all shivery, so then I had to go and find Skip who told me that Joe was suffering from hyperthermia. Anyway, it all went on a bit but the ending is that Joe has had to go home cos he was then sick. So that's two camps for Joe and two early trips home. I wasn't too bothered as I now have / had a tent to myself. I Lynx Africad (the Scout deodorant of choice according to Matthew) the tent to take the smell away and rearranged my roll-mat and sleeping

77

bag. However, I was not alone for long. Skip had to commander a tent to use as the sick bay as apparently Aaron had been sick in the night and his parents weren't able to come and pick him up until later so he had to be insulated. Aaron is Hawks' assistant petrol leader. I now have Josh in with me in case Aaron has germs. I hope that Josh doesn't lead me ashtray. Josh put his head inside my tent whilst I was reorganising everything and said that it smelt like a girl's toilet. How Josh knows what a girl's toilet smells like I will never know. I told him that it was Joe's aftershave. Then he said that it smelt like the public bar of the The Woodman which is a pub. I've no idea how Josh knows what the inside of a pub smells like. I expect he's just making it all up.

Josh has no kit. He said that he turned up in his uniform but has no kit and no bedding. Skip doesn't know. Josh said that his mummy told him to sort himself out but he didn't realise that that meant clothes and sleeping bag as well and she didn't seem to wonder why he had no rucksack. He's going to be smellier than Joe. Maybe I should lend him some of my clothes.

He doesn't have any shoes either. He jumped in the car to come here and cos he was late he thought he would put them on in the car. But he forgot. But when he arrived at the camp car park he got out and was just about to walk round to the other side of the car to say goodbye to his mummy when she just drove off. He's been left kit-less (although he didn't pack any) and shoe-less (although he did have some, but only on the way here and even then not on his feet).

After breakfast I had to be put in a roped-off safety area. This is because I had to learn how to use an axe, saw or knife

78

safely. There has to be a roped-off bit so that no one comes too near and gets their fingers chopped, sawn or anything else cut off. I wanted to do everything properly so that I wasn't a danger to myself otherwise I would have had to have called Gary and reported myself as being a danger to myself. This would not have been a very clever thing to do. He couldn't remove me from mummy and daddy for something I had done I don't think otherwise loads of children would be chopping their fingers off and stuff like that. I tried all three. These are three very useful skills as Skip said that we're going to make go-karts soon and no one else in Woodpeckers (plus one Kestrel) will know what to do. I think that Skip meant that how to use a saw was the best one as I can't think we will be making go karts with axes or knives. When it was Josh's turn with the axe, he let out a what Skip called a blood-curdling yell as he brought the axe down on what Skip called an unsuspecting twig on the chopping block which was a tree stump. Skip told him that he was preparing kindling and logs, not getting ready to guillotine someone and could he put something on his feet? Josh then answered back, something that Skip doesn't really like. Barnaby answered back once and Skip said Better to remain silent and be thought a fool than to speak out and remove all doubt, Abraham Lincoln. I think for a moment Skip had forgotten Barnaby's name. Josh told Skip that as it was a survival camp he may have to behead a squirrel or a pigeon or something and to do it really quickly. Skip told Josh not to be so stupid as we don't do that sort of thing in Scouts. Then he told Skip that he was trying to survive without anything on his feet. "Whatever," said Skip and walked off. I think Skip's a bit fed up with Josh and he hasn't even slept with him. Neither have I, yet. Jake told Josh that he did have to behead a pigeon in Scouts once.

Apparently Jake had done something called "I'm a Scout, get me out of here" with the district Scouts. This is where Scouts have a series of challenges to complete. The last one was gutting a pigeon but Jake said that he chopped its head off as well. He didn't use his axe though as he couldn't get hold of one so he used his penknife. He took the head home and stuck it to the back of one of his mum's drinks coasters, drilled a hole through it (the coaster not the pigeon head) and hung it on his bedroom wall like a trophy kill but a Scout version. He said that he got the coaster out of the drawer that his mummy keeps stuff in for best cos she never uses stuff from it, but when she went upstairs to say goodnight to him and saw the mounted pigeon head she had a screamy moment. Jake thought it was the pigeon that was the problem, but it wasn't. She said, "What the sweary word do you think you're up to? You've stuck that bird's head on one of my sweary blue agate coasters. They're hand-made in Italy and very, very expensive." "So am I," said Jake without stopping to think what he was saying. Anyway, pigeon-head is still on Jake's wall and he told his mummy that when it shrivels up completely and drops off she can have her coaster back.

Barnaby had to go to hospital this morning. The Big Nipper obviously did its stuff. When Barnaby snuggled deep down into his sleeping bag in the middle of the night, he set off the Big Nipper and it broke one of his toes. Result! He even managed to last through the night with it but I don't think he got much sleep. I don't think Skip was very pleased as he had to send Gunner to A & E with Barnaby, but he started it. Barnaby had a bandage round his toes and couldn't get his shoe on so he was hopping everywhere. Skip got very cross and this morning demanded to know which Scout had set the trap. I was afraid so I said nothing. Now I've lost the trap as Skip has confiscated it and I could hardly ask for it back. Skip said that he's going to get it fingerprinted which is okay cos Joe was holding it earlier.

Eventually Barnaby had to go home because he told Skip that he would have nightmares if he had to put his toes inside his sleeping bag again. I suggested that he wore his hiking boots to bed but Skip told me that that was a stupid idea. But it wouldn't have been a stupid idea if I had put another torture in his tent. But I couldn't because torture number one had been confiscated and torture number two didn't exist. Barnaby wore the same clothes home that he wore to camp yesterday. Despite the fact that he had changed and was always in warm and dry clothes as we're always being told, he said that he liked to freak his mummy out when she picked him up because she would think that he hadn't got changed at all. On the other hand, I don't think Hugo has changed at all so far but he did get all his clothes out this afternoon and kick them round the campsite in the mud for a few minutes so that his mummy would think that he had been changing each day and was in warm and dry clothes all the time.

Aaron's been sick. His tent had been drinking double-concentrate orange squash without water with whisky. He's not going home though cos no one knows where his mummy is. I expect she's shopping.

There's a cockerel running around the campsite. Laura says it's hers and its name is Isambard. He's quite friendly and it's funny cos I had a dream about Isambard. He wasn't a chicken though, he was a boy although I can't remember what he looked like.

**Saturday 7th March**
**Skip**
**Lunchtime**
I had only just got to sleep when there was a piercing scream, the sort that demands instant attention. I sat up in my bag and could hear a loud whimpering so had to get dressed and go and investigate. It was Josh in the patrol tent with Barnaby, Jake and Hugo. "What's the matter?" I whispered through the canvas. I needn't have bothered speaking quietly as they were all fully awake. "Josh is trying to pee in a Perrier bottle and he's got his todger stuck," said Jake. Followed by the inevitable, "Can you come and help, please, Skip?" Now this could have crossed so many safeguarding boundaries that I didn't know quite where to start. In the end I said to the canvas, "If you can't get it out then I'll have to come in and chop it off." It was my intention to cut round the bottle as high up as I dared and then send Josh off to A & E with Gunner. However, my threat of cutting Josh's todger off (which is what I later learnt he thought I was going to do), was enough to free Josh from his additional plastic appendage and everyone went back to bed. It was just unfortunate that Josh forgot to put the lid back on the Perrier bottle before he climbed back into his sleeping bag.

I woke up this morning at 5am with Isambard cock – a – doodle - dooing so loudly that I thought that he was inside my tent. Then I sat up and found that he was. He had managed to get under the side of the mess tent which hadn't been pegged down and into my tent that hadn't been zipped up. Silly me. He then decided to put a large motion on the (sewn-in) groundsheet before jumping up onto my rucksack that was propped up in the corner and cock – a – doodle - dooing again. I was now beginning to understand how Mrs xxxxx had been feeling, even though I was probably at a much closer distance. After all, I don't expect she actually had a cock in her bedroom.

There was no way that I was going back to sleep so I got up, got dressed with Isambard watching which is a bit unnerving, picked him up and took him to the mess tent. Once inside I gave Isambard some cornflakes. Despite my best efforts I cannot get the Scouts to eat cornflakes on camp unless they're covered in sugar. Even then they don't really like them. "That's all Frosties are," I tell them. "Cornflakes with sugar," but they're not the same apparently.

After Isambard had had a little nibble I picked him up again, took him outside and plopped him on top of Gunner's Force 10 [ridge tent]. "Do your worst, Isambard," I whispered. Isambard threw back his head. "COCK – A – DOODLE - DOO" he screamed. "COCK – A – DOODLE - DOO!" There was absolutely no response from inside the tent so I picked Isambard up and slowly unzipped the fly-sheet then the inner door, creating just enough of a hole to push Isambard through. He squawked and flapped his wings as I zipped up after him and retired several paces, as if I had just lit some sort of blue touch paper, and retired to wait for the firework to spring into life. "COCK – A – DOODLE - DOO! COCK – A – DOODLE - DOO!" came a not very muffled noise from inside the tent. Gunner must have been getting deafened. Maybe I should have hidden? Just as I was cogitating, from behind me, just inside the edge of the woods, came a, "AND

– A – GOOD – MORNING – TO - YOU!" but with a distinctly human ring to it. I went into the woods to see who it was and found Gunner snuggled up inside his sleeping bag, suspended in a hammock a few feet off the ground, cuddling Teresa who was looking equally cosy, smirking. "Why aren't you in your tent?" I demanded. "Cos I knew you would try a trick on me like that with Isambard. I know you." "That's most unfair. I wouldn't have thought of it if Isambard hadn't broken out of the mess tent and into mine this morning." "He didn't break out of the mess tent," said Gunner. "I went and got him and shoved him in your tent before you did the same to me. And," he continued, "if you tip us out of my hammock I will kill you, real, seriously kill you." It was time to back off.

Gunner and Crusher were on breakfast supervision duty so I decided to go for a wander in order to lick my wounds. I found myself searching for a trendy rock-star t-shirt to match Gunner's. In nearby Biggin Hill I discovered a vintage clothes shop. The only suitable t-shirt I could find was one bearing the Rolling Stones' iconic large tongue logo. The shirt was a medium so was a bit small on me but it didn't matter. I think the Scouts liked it and they must reckon that they now have two really cool dudes for Scout leader and ASL. Whilst in Biggin Hill I found out about a farm locally that takes unwanted small animals. We can take Isambard there this afternoon. I must remember to tell Laura that that's what we'll do: he will be looked after there and she can visit him at any time.

I got back to camp to find Alex presenting me with three quarters of a bottle of whisky and a sick Joe. Goodness knows where the whisky had been, with a label that had felt-tipped scribble all over it, but I'm not drinking it. Joe was soaked through and said that he had had a shower. I really don't know what's going on with that boy. I rang his mother and told her that she would have to come and pick up Joe because he had been sick. "Or are you at the theatre again?" I asked her. "My dear Mr Hemming-Clark," she replied haughtily. "Die Fledermaus may go on a bit but not for over six weeks."

During the night Aaron was also sick. He told me that it may have been something he had drunk, but he still needed to go home. I had remembered to tell the Scouts that if they needed to wake me up in the night because of an emergency, then they needed to come to the orange tent. I then sleep in the blue one. I'll normally wake up but I won't have to get up up, just sit up and make sure that it sounds like everything's under control. Aaron found what he thought was my tent and started calling out, "Skip! Skip." This succeeded in waking up Crusher who then had to go and clear the mess up whilst I pretended to be asleep. This morning whilst I was out Crusher took it upon himself to ring Aaron's parents up to ask them to come and pick him up. When his mother asked, "What, now?" Crusher told her, "Yes, now" otherwise he would ring social services. This is our new line of attack for parents who think that "now" means anything other than "straightaway". Aaron's mother then asked Crusher if she could speak to me, which she couldn't because I was busy. i.e. shopping. Crusher told me that she was slurring her words quite a bit as if she were forcing each word out. "It's – a – bit – difficult," she said, slowly and methodically. "Are you okay?" Crusher asked, thinking that she must have decided to hit the bottle for breakfast, having just received some great shock like, "Where's my son? He's not in his bed," having forgotten that he had been sent on camp. "Yes - I'm - fine, but - I'm – in – New – York – and - it's – half – past – four – in – the - morning." I couldn't believe it! They've dumped Aaron on camp and gone swanning off to New York for the weekend. Not London, or Margate, or Sevenoaks, or even Paris. New York! "Well, is your husband happy with your leaving your sick son on camp?" Crusher asked. "Why don't you have a quick word with him first?" "That's kinda difficult," she slurred. "He thinks I'm in Manchester."

If that were that, things would have been okay, relatively speaking. But that wasn't that. In the morning, whilst Gunner was clearing up sick, Barnaby found him and told him that he had broken his toe and so Gunner came and told me as I walked back into the campsite that he was now going to have cart Barnaby off to hospital. Someone had set a rat trap and put it down his sleeping bag. Nobody owned up to it so I told them I was going to get it fingerprinted. This would usually flush out the culprit but nobody said a thing. Barnaby was hobbling around and kept saying he was in pain so after he returned from the hospital all bandaged up I got him sent home.

In the meantime I had to take Nico out of Aaron's tent and make Aaron's tent the sick bay. I then had to put Nico in with Barnaby, Jake and Hugo and take Josh out because Josh and Barnaby don't really get on with each other, and put Josh in with Alex after Joe had vacated his place by going home. Then Barnaby went home so I could have kept Josh in the patrol tent anyway. I think that is how it went. Talk about musical tents. Not that it matters much as they're in hammocks tonight.

The Scouts were taught safety with axes and saws this morning. They listened and performed well, apart from Josh who decided to back-chat me so he got a staring at.

## Saturday 7th March
## Skip
## Night-time
This afternoon the Scouts made shelters out of scavenged materials and we taught them how to make hammocks. They were given a tarpaulin each and were told that they could go and camp anywhere they liked within the site, within reason, so most of them have disappeared into the woods for the night. I might even get a lie-in. Earlier on we took most of them into Biggin Hill and gave them a few quid each and told them to source their food from one of the supermarkets which they then had to bring back, prepare, cook and eat. I was taking no chances. Gunner, Crusher and I had a curry.

They were put into small teams and whilst one member from each team stayed behind to get their fire ready, Crusher and I took the others shopping. They didn't do too badly. Alex's team had loads of food - they must have shopped wisely. Tegan's team did a great pudding because they didn't have to spend any money on meat. Hugo's team had cereal and salad. I'm sure I told them that they had to get something that they had to cook. At least no one appears to have been poisoned and, after the excitement of last night, this one seems pretty calm. We awarded first prize to the girls – agaaaain!

Josh is still wearing his Scout shirt. He's had it on for a day and a half now. I suggested to him that he might like to change it as it will be starting to pong soon. "Whatever," was his fulsome reply.

Isambard's gone walkabout. I told Laura my plan and she's more than happy with the outcome. I've told her to tell her parents what we're going to do and that they can go and get him back from the farm if they disagree. Cockerels do disappear from time to time, according to Laura. We'll find him alright in the morning, that's for sure. Even if he's a mile away we'll know where he is. We'll hear him. Look out, Crusher – your tent is next! A great camp! What fun!

## Saturday 7th March
## Night-time
## Alex

There was change of plan this afternoon although Skip may have known cos he had loads of rope and stuff for hammocks and showed us how to make them. As part of the survival badge we've had to make a shelter out of salvaged materials and sleep in it. I can do this as I've done it at home in my bedroom. I went out with Josh, Nico and Jake this afternoon and found loads of plastic tubes in the woods. We collected over one hundred. We cut them all lengthways and opened them out and flattened them. Then we made holes in the corners and threaded them together with string that Josh said that he had "acquired," like a piece of armour. We then slung it over some rope that was tied between two trees. We then added a tarp for extra waterproofing and made our hammocks. Piece of cake. Job done. Before that Nico, Jake and me we went into Biggin Hill and bought food for cooking while Josh did the fire. We were going to do vegetable kebabs on skewers cos Josh is a vegetarian although he was eating sosages this morning but he said that he couldn't eat chicken after seeing Isambard running around. Anyway, my team came back with some vegetables and loads of sweets cos we hadn't spent much money cos we didn't have to buy any sosages or steak or fish or any stuff like that which is really expensive. Laura's a vegetarian so I expected the girl's team would get loads of sweets as well but they didn't they bought stuff and made a pudding. They bought bananas and cut them longways without taking off the skins, then they put loads of chocolate buttons in and then closed them up and wrapped them in tin foil (three layers) and put them in the embers. Yummy!

We got our hammocks up and cos Nico had a spare sleeping bag and a spare spare sleeping bag we put them on the ground to warm the ground up under our hammocks cos Skip says that you need insulation on the ground when you're camping. I expect this is the same even when you're a few feet off the ground but who knows. Then Nico and me we went and started washing and peeling and chopping the vegetables cos we couldn't find Josh and Jake said he was going to get our fire ready. After we chopped up the veg which we did really quickly cos it only took an hour Jake called out to us and said that the fire was going well and we needed to thread the skewers and get cooking. We went off into the woods and the fire was ready for cooking with nice embers and stuff but no Josh. Then Jake said that he had found him and he was coming and then he appeared out of nowhere with a "TA DA!" and he was holding a chopping board with on it a CHICKEN! Not a one like you buy in Sainsbury's with string and neat and in cellophane but this one was like it had been in a hurricane and had all its clothes blown off and was chilly with goose bumps or I suppose chicken bumps and NO HEAD and I said to Josh, What is that and he said CHICKEN! TA DA! And I said I thought you were a veggie and he said only to throw Skip off the scent and then I asked Where did you get the chicken from and he said GUESS? And I said Oh no, I don't think I want to and he said GUESS? And I said No so he said It's Isambard and I went OH NO! again. And he said Oh yes AND we've got loads of sweets as well.

It was time to have a little sit down.

Josh then told us that when we had gone shopping Gunner had said that he was going for a snooze in his hammock so Josh went and got an axe from the mess tent and went and put it in the roped-off area. Then he went and got some Coco-Pops for Isambard but he didn't like them so he got some Corn Flakes cos there were loads of those and he went and poured them in the roped-off safety area on the chopping stump. Then Isambard came over, cluck, cluck, cluck and started to eat the Corn Flakes off the stump so Josh picked up the axe and said have a nice day and then went CHOP CHOP CHOP and he said he chopped his head straight off but that wasn't the end cos then Isambard started to run around and blood was squirting out of his head like a chocolate fountain only it was red and Josh was shouting Isambard, Isambard but then Josh realised that he (Isambard) couldn't hear cos Isambard was running towards the mess tent and anyway his head with his ears were on the chopping block so then Gunner shouted What are you doing but he didn't open his eyes (thank goodness) and Josh said he was looking for Isambard which was true cos well probably better to say looking AT Isambard well part of him anyway. Then Isambard stopped (the bit with no head) and then just went UGH! but I think that that was a Josh noise and not an Isambard noise cos Isambard couldn't talk out of his neck and then he (Isambard) fell over. So now Josh has got hold of one of Nico's sleeping bags and put it over Isambard and taken him into the woods. And no one's seen. Well Josh said that he thought Teresa saw cos she was in the hammock with Gunner but she had her eyes screwed up really tightly like she had seen a ghost which she had sort of so she's not going to say anything.

So then Josh went back to the roped-off safety area and the head is sitting there so what does he do with it? He got a mug from the mess tent and put Isambard's head in it and now it's in Jake's tent and Jake's going to put it in his wash bag and take it home. I do hope he takes it out before his mum does a wash bag inspection. It would give her a bit of a fright otherwise.

Josh then had to scuff the ground up all around to cover all the blood which he said was painful with nothing on his feet but he managed. There was blood on the chopping block stump but not much and on the axe but Josh just put that back in the mess tent. The next person that uses it will get a bit of a shock cos they'll think that someone's been executed (which they have actually, well something).

Gosh, can you imagine all this work for just one chicken? Can you imagine how much you would have to do if you chopped a human's head off and they went running round shouting I've had my head chopped off, I've had my head chopped off with loads more blood that you've got to hide. Actually thinking about it you wouldn't shout anything cos

91

your mouth would be on the chopping block and your lungs would be on the other bit. No wonder most murderers get found out and are in prison.

Then Jake found Josh but they got a bit stuck cos Josh had found a little woods to hide in then he found that it was in the middle of the go-kart track so they had to wait until the go-karts had finished whizzing round. Still, they've been busy plucking Isambard that's why we couldn't find them and then the go-karts stopped and they've put the feathers on the fire. Then Josh pulled off Isambard's neck and took all his insides out cos he looked at what to do on Google cos the one thing that he does have is the one thing that he's not allowed to have, i.e. a phone. So all his insides are on the fire as well. Now all we had to do was cut up Isambard and put bits on the skewers and it was all a bit off a mess. Then Skip came over and asked how we were getting on and we said fine and he said you're making a bit of mess of that chicken and why didn't we just buy fillets cos that would have been much easier but we didn't want fillets we wanted chicken and Skip looked a bit puzzled and said you don't often see chickens with their feet still on so Josh told him that we i.e. me had bought it from the organic counter and Skip went oh cool and that was that. After that we fried Isambard's feet cos Josh found that on Google as well but they didn't taste very nice still it's survival unlike bananas and chocolate which isn't although we all then ate our sweets but that was okay cos we had survived.

Skip's now been wearing a t-shirt with a large tongue on it which is rather rude as well as quite unsuitable for a Scout camp. It's also too small for him. Maybe he didn't pack enough clothes and is now on to his emergency wardrobe.

## Sunday 8th March
## Alex

Back home after our survival camp. Josh, Jake, Nico and I we survived last night without being murdered but it poured with rain and our shelter leaked. This meant that at half past one at night we evacuated ourselves and put ourselves into my tent with Josh. Although Barnaby had gone home Jake and Nico said that they didn't want to go back to their tent in case someone was inside booby trapping more sleeping bags with another Big Nipper. I told them that there was only one and that it was me and that I was responsible for torturing Barnaby and that it had been confiscated. And they wanted to know why I had brought a Big Nipper on survival camp cos no one was going to cook any rats so I said that Skip had told us to bring sleeping bags and tortures and then they all laughed and Jake waved his torch in the air and said here's a torture and I thought oh dear. I told them not to tell Skip but they still wouldn't go back to their tent so they came in with me and Josh cos they said that they didn't want to sleep with Isambard's head but Josh told them he was dead and mostly eaten but they said that that was worse. A two man tent is made for one man or one and a half boys and there were four of us so it was a real squash and we had to do it with me and Josh up one end and Jake and Nico up the other end and our feet sort of met in the middle but we were dry but a bit smelly cos Josh was in the sleeping bag that he had put Isambard in earlier.

When we woke up we had to get our breakfasts ready. We had been given eggs, bacon and beans for cooking and pots and pans and other bits. We had billies which are pots for Scouts. Josh said that he was a vegetarian again, which he wasn't, especially after half an Isambard but it meant that he got a huge tin of beans instead of egg and bacon. Well, he got egg and bacon as well cos he told Gunner that he was a vegetarian so got the beans after he had got the eggs and bacon from Skip. When we did our practice at the Scout Hut Skip told us that to cook beans without getting a billy messy we could choose to open the tin and put it in the embers or put it whole in a billy with loads of water. Josh was in charge of beans while I went and said "Hallo" to Chloe who seemed to have spent most of the camp asleep. I had only been chatting to her for a couple of minutes when there was a huge great big explosion and Skip and Gunner went running into the woods. I followed them back but I went slowly in case there was blood or someone was dead. When I got to our little camp we found Josh completely covered in ash. Our fire had disappeared and the baked bean tin was lying on the ground smoking. Nico's two sleeping bags that we had left out all night and so were soaking wet and muddy so we had hung them over the tarp to dry were covered in orange sauce and thousands of beans. "Please, Skip," said Josh, looking as though he needed his mummy, "Do you have a fork?"

After all that excitement and Josh having to suddenly not be a vegetarian again so he could have something for breakfast (I think his second vegetarian period was the shortest ever cos it lasted about nine minutes) everything else was going to be not so exciting on the rest of this camp. Or so we thought!

Unfortunately there was no orange juice for breakfast. Someone, mentioning no names, had decided to spend yesterday topping up his water bottle with orange juice instead of water and was then selling it to the others on the camp site, along with pieces of cake that his mummy had made, instead of handing it in.

After breakfast we had to clear up all the rope and tarps and stuff from the woods. It went on forever! Josh did a poo in a tree and got into big trouble. Mind you, I don't think he did the other one. That's a bit of a mystery.

We had to do a litter sweep before we left camp. It was very successful. We were all given a black sack to fill. Josh went and got the bin from the toilet and filled his black sack up in one go then put a few things on top to make it look as if it was all rubbish from the campsite and not just paper hand towels so he won a prize for the most litter picked. Top work, Josh! Skip wasn't so impressed with all the plastic tubes that we collected that we hadn't used for our survival shelter though.

Big problems in the laundry department this afternoon. Mummy has been busy washing all the stuff I brought back from camp. My sleeping bag got VIP treatment in the washing machine as there was no room for anything else. Fortunately she didn't notice the holes. Then wash number two was the rest. How was I to know all my badges would come off? How was I to know that you needed special glue to stick them onto a Scout shirt? I 'phoned Hugo and he told me that you can't use normal glue. So what's now happened is that my camp clothes are drying all over the house but they all have stringy bits of glue all over them, like someone's been wiping their bogeys over everything. Needless to say, my Scout shirt does not look very happy at all as it now has no badges over it. Maybe I won't earn any badges, then there will be none to sew (stick) on.

Scottie Dog's moaning that it's like a sauna underneath my bed. I told him to stop complaining. At least he's warm, and alive, unlike Isambard. And he doesn't have a broken microwave on his conscience.

## Sunday 8th March
### Skip

So much for a good night's sleep. Alex and Josh *et al's* so called waterproof shelter wasn't and so at 1.30am I had Alex outside my tent in hysterics, crying, "I'm wet and I've nowhere to sleep!" Quite why he couldn't just get back in his tent, I've no idea. So I had to get up, get dressed, put my boots on, put a coat on, find my torch and go and sort him and Josh and the other two out. For some reason they all wanted to go in Alex's tent; they would certainly have been cosy. I had just got back in my tent, dried myself, undressed and got back in my sleeping bag and feeling snug and warm when I felt the desperate urge to go to the toilet. I couldn't believe it! I was going to have to get back up, get dressed, put my boots on, put a coat on, find my torch and walk a couple of hundred metres just for a pee. Fortunately I know what to do. Keep an empty Lucozade bottle to hand. Lucozade bottles have the added advantage of having a wider neck to avoid any trapping of the organ such as Josh suffered the night before. The fact that it was raining was an added advantage otherwise another leader might wake and think that the camp site had suddenly sprung a leak or gained a waterfall. The only problem was that I had already filled my Lucozade bottle; it was a number two that I now desperately needed. I was in unfamiliar territory but still desperate not to have to leave the tent. The plastic bottle was just not going to work, whichever way I looked at it. In the end I found a small plastic carrier bag. It would have to do. I got out of my sleeping bag, positioned myself as one would in the traditional (i.e. all the ones I seem to find when on holiday) French toilets and did my business. I tied a little knot in the bag and unzipped the tent. It was pitch black! I flung the bag and its contents outside. I could sort it out in the morning. A few baby wipes and some hand sani. later and I was back in my sleeping bag and asleep. Again.

I woke up at about seven o'clock and all I could hear was giggling. The Scouts couldn't be up already, could they? I got out of my sleeping bag and stuck my head outside the tent. There, hanging from the branch of an oak tree a few feet away was my, er, deposit. Jake, Josh, Nico and Alex were standing round it giggling. "It's probably a dog walker who can't be bothered to take their dog mess home," I called out. "But Skip," said Alex, "Dogs aren't allowed on our campsites." "Okay, well I'll find out later. Go and get your breakfasts ready." I would have to discreetly move it later when no one was around.

Whilst the Scouts were preparing for breakfast and I was just about to go and decant my Lucozade, there was a horrendous explosion from the direction of the woods. This is the stuff of nightmares for a Scout leader. We can deal with first aid, even up to cardiac arrests and severe bleeding but if a Scout has blown himself up... Gunner came running. "Quick!" I said and we ran to where the noise came from. I left my Lucozade bottle next to my tent for when I returned.

It has to be said that Josh did look a bit shell-shocked, but other than that he seemed okay. His fire appeared to have blown up and there were beans everywhere, like one of those gingerbread houses we get the Scouts to decorate at Christmas, only instead of Smarties we had beans. Before I could say anything, Josh asked, rather pathetically, "Please, Skip, do you have a fork?" I thought that we were entitled to an explanation first. Needless to say the reason for the explosion was quite straightforward. I had taught the Scouts a while ago to simmer a tin of condensed milk in a billy-full of water to make caramel or pierce the top of a baked bean can and put it in the embers to cook the beans but not to put any tin directly on the fire unopened. Josh said that he had got a bit muddled up with the result that he put the unpierced tin in the embers and sure enough, it exploded. It would have made a very interesting accident report, hit by flying baked beans, but fortunately Josh was not standing near the fire at the time, so all we had to do was wipe down a couple of trees.

I went back to our camp and couldn't find my Lucozade bottle so instead I went and extracted my "dog" poop bag and flushed it down the toilet. I returned to the mess tent and went inside where I found Crusher sitting with Josh who was nestling a mug of something. Josh still looked in a state of shock. "He was feeling a bit faint," said Crusher, "so I brought him in here and gave him some of your Lucozade." Before I could say anything, not that I knew what I was actually going to say, but sensing my own sense of shock, he quickly added, "I hope you don't mind." It was going to be one of those incidents that I was never ever going to be able to tell him, or anyone else for that matter, and one of the main reasons why, dear diary, you are indeed, very, very private.

After breakfast a quick litter sweep of the area turned into a full dismantling of the site as the Scouts had managed to build several shelters each with rope tied to random trees here and there, tarpaulins flapping around in the wind, some hammocks attached to the trees, some lying half finished on the ground, string everywhere. We went deep into the woods in a long scouring line and we organised the clearing up of several more bivis and then went even deeper into the woods. We were getting further and further away from civilisation but still finding pieces of rope lying around or tied to trees. We reached almost as far as we could go when I stopped by a large oak. It had been pollarded many years ago. The branches had grown out leaving a platform at adult eye-height that would have made quite a good camping spot. There appeared to be a fair bit of blood on the ground as if a small-scale massacre had been taking place. As we passed the oak I heard Alex say quietly to Tegan, "That's where Josh did his poo." I pulled Alex aside and whispered to him, "What did you say?" Having repeated himself I called Josh over. Whilst Alex wandered back down the line I peered onto the tree platform. There was indeed a poo there, but I was willing to think that it could have been a deer poo, albeit from a fairly acrobatic deer. "Josh," I asked, "Have you done a poo in this tree?" "No, Skip." I would have to put my 'fingerprint' hat on. "Oh, dear, Josh, that's a pity, because now I'm going to have to gather up the evidence to get it DNA-tested. Now then, I'll ask you once more. Is that your poo?" "Yes, Skip" said Josh without even looking at it. I couldn't believe it! Not only had one of my Scouts pooed in a tree, but he had also fallen for my DNA-testing suggestion. "What on earth were you doing, pooing in a tree?" I asked him incredulously. "Well, Skip, I was desperate for the toilet and the toilet was so far away that I didn't think I'ld reach it

in time." "So you went in a tree?" "Yes, Skip. Sorry, Skip."
"So now you're going to have to walk 'far away' to the toilet,
get some toilet paper, come all the way back, scoop up your
poo, go back 'far away' to the toilet, flush it down where you
should have put it in the first place, wash your hands
thoroughly and then come back to our camp site so that we
can go on our mini-hike." As I wandered over to catch the
others up I heard Josh say to himself, "Well at least I don't
leave mine hanging in a tree" but I thought that enough had
been said already, and I didn't really need to add, "You
know that Lucozade that you had earlier? Guess what..." so I
didn't. But I was very tempted.

When I caught up with the others Alex sidled over to me and
asked quietly, "You won't tell Josh that it was me that told
you, will you, Skip? The thing is," he added, without waiting
for my reply, "when he told us last night that he had done a
poo in a tree, we thought he was joking." "Unfortunately,
Alex, he wasn't," was all I could say by way of reply.

Having cleared the area of tarps, rope and string, now we
could start work on the litter, with prizes for the most
collected. Josh did really well, probably to make amends for
his earlier indiscretion, so "Well done, Josh" and he got a
prize. However, he did go a little too far. Alex and he came
up and told me, looking very pleased with themselves,
"Skip, we've collected up loads of plastic tubes that were
sticking up out of the ground and making the place look all
messy. We used some for our scavenger shelter and here's
the rest of them," they said, dumping around a hundred of
the tubes at my feet. "Err, they may be messy-making plastic
tubes to you, boys, but they're also tree protectors."

It was time to disappear. Isambard would just have to fend for himself. Hopefully he would still be able to; I was having my doubts.

It took the usual several hours to get everything packed up, drive to the Scout Hut, unpack, hang up tents to dry and get back home. I hadn't been in more than ten minutes when off went the 'phone again. "Beep, beep, beep, beep, BEEEEEEEP!" The day was not complete without another text. From Nico's mother. Again! "Thanks for a great weekend! Nico really enjoyed himself! He's fast asleep in bed! Mind you, you are also, probably! When you have five minutes Nico has some missing kit: A racing green Hunter wellie (left foot) with his surname written inside top, a red Vango sleeping mat thing and black bag – I think they were named, a blue plastic fork (unnamed), twenty pounds and five hot chocolate sachets. Let me know when you find it. Now, go and have a beer. Mind you, you're probably on your sixth by now - I know I am (wine, not beer! Plus a couple of vodkas!) See you next Friday. Love Sue xxxxx P.S. Sorry I couldn't stay and help clear up. I would have done if I was on my own but Morgan needed picking up from the pub where he'd been all afternoon! Alright for some, that's what I say!!!!!!!!" Yeah, "Alright for some indeed." Five minutes later she was back. "Just going through Nico's washing. What on earth have you been doing with these kids? Two of his sleeping bags are soaking wet and covered in mud and beans, the other one is full of blood. I thought I was sending him on a camp not a World War I re-enactment. And who taught him to light his farts? Sue." (no kisses). This time I had to reply. I texted, "Hi Sue. At least he's still alive, unlike some of the other less fortunate ones. Ask him about Isambard." I didn't get a further reply.

## Thursday 12th March
## Alex

A sweary day today. Mummy's credit card statement has arrived and there are two entries, one after the other, from the same online shop. The first one, dated 7th February, was for £5.39, the second, which was dated 28th February, was for £45.79. First she accused daddy of using her credit card and when he denied it she said that she was going to call the police as she had been scammed. I then had to explain to mummy that that was probably my Woodpecker badge which had been delivered quickly so as not to cause any upset at Scouts. "Never mind Scouts," she cried, "what about my (sweary) credit card that you think that you can just dip into when you feel like it?" There was no answer to this, so I didn't give one. I just told her that it was a small price to pay for my life to be saved. Mummy then said that the (sweary) Woodpecker badge cost more than my (sweary) sleeping bag. This is a bit unfair as I know that my sleeping bag was the cheapest one in the shop. Had she bought one that was a little bit more, like the one I suggested would be good, like the goose down one that I suggested which was just under seven hundred pounds, then my badge wouldn't have been more expensive. So it's her fault. What's "down" anyway? It's probably some special part of a goose like its intestines, so the sleeping bag is probably full of goose intestines which would keep you nice and warm. They probably have to be dried first though. Anyway, it's too late to upgrade to a more expensive one now. Mummy said that mine was "bedroom soiled" although as far as I know I haven't soiled it yet. Just put loads of holes in it. I didn't think that this was a good time to tell her that though.

**Thursday 12th March**
**Skip**
I've sorted out all the lost property from camp and there is so much of it! There are several items per Scout at least. There's underwear (that no one ever claims) including some very frilly knickers, four pairs of trousers, SEVEN t-shirts, two mugs, thirteen pieces of cutlery, a designer jacket which is the only thing with a name on it, but it's someone's name that isn't one of my Scouts, a camera, a pair of waterproof trousers, a rabbit (stuffed), a dinosaur onesie and a fire-extinguisher.

I've now had a letter (a letter! She must mean business!) through my door from Jake's mum. She's written to tell me that she doesn't need to name any of Jake's stuff because she's so busy and so, as everyone else should be naming their own Scout's stuff, anything that is left behind that isn't named must be Jake's. I've emailed her and said that all the unnamed stuff is at the Scout Hut including a pair of pink frilly knickers with "Maid of Honour" printed on them and that I presume they're Jake's and should I give them to him at Scouts tomorrow? As of tonight I have had no response.

**Friday 13th March**
**Alex**
It had been troubling me all week about why it would be funny calling Jimmy, "Pussy" so I asked Skip. He just grinned, again, and said that the word was "Pusser," which was a simplification of "Purser" who is the man who looks after the money. This is a bit of a relief as I was beginning to wonder why anyone would want to be named after a ship's cat. It's almost as bad as being called "Dogger" after the

ship's dog, not that there were many of those around in the old days, whereas the ship's cat would have had a useful function as a mouser. Or maybe a "musser". Ha, ha.

Jake wasn't at Scouts tonight. Hugo said that he's not allowed to come for one week cos when he got home from camp he put Isambard on another of his mum's coasters and has hung him on his wall next to the pigeon but he's had to stick Isambard's head on sideways cos there wasn't much of his neck to stick so now Isambard looks like he's looking out of his bedroom window unlike the pigeon who is looking across the room. Jake told Hugo that he likes Isambard more cos he thinks that the pigeon is looking at him while he's getting dressed but I wouldn't have worried about that myself. I expect pigeons have seen far worse. Well, live ones anyway.

I hope Laura never goes into Jake's bedroom. She would see something in there that would cause her to faint at the very least and at the most would probably give her hysterics. I think I should warn her.

## Friday 13th March
### Skip
I put a photo of the plastic tubes that Alex and Josh collected whilst on camp on Facebook, along with a caption that said, "Just back from a weekend's camping at a Scout site that will have to remain anonymous for now. As part of the Outdoor Challenge Award Scouts have to, 'Provide a service commitment to the site for about an hour.' We were asked to do litter picking. The Scouts worked hard and filled several black sacks. After half an hour one team came up and told us, looking very pleased with themselves, 'Skip,

we've collected up loads of plastic tubes that were sticking up out of the ground and making the place look all messy.' 'Err, they may be messy making plastic tubes to you, but they're also tree protectors.' As far as I'm aware, that particular team is still at the camp site, slowly locating and then putting back the guards, one by one, over the saplings that they were, until this morning, quietly and competently protecting."

I've received several comments, including one that read, "Well we planted about two hundred saplings at our district xxxxx site near Biggin Hill. Twelve months on there are almost none to be seen. We think the deer ate the canes, leaving the plastic tubes scattered around the woods."

Poor old deer. They nearly got the blame for pooing in a tree, now they're being blamed for the plastic tubes disappearing. Head down time!

I awarded Josh his "Community Impact Badge" tonight. "What's this for?" he asked as he came up to receive it. "Services to an oak tree," I said as I saluted, shook his left hand and presented the badge. Josh looked confused. The other Scouts giggled.

Jake wasn't at Scouts tonight which was just as well as he might have been going home with a pair of not his knickers. "I think these are your mother's," I was going to say. That would have got the Chislehurst tongues wagging, and more than usual which is saying something.

**Sunday 15th March**
**Alex**

One good thing about Scout camp emerged today. Mummy and daddy were talking over dinner and mummy was going on about her credit card bill again. Daddy said that she shouldn't worry about it as Scouting is very good value for money, that is to say not much, and the fact that my Scouting achievements will look good on my C of E. Mummy then agreed and said that the last camp cost only £40 which she thought was a great price for a weekend's babysitting. This isn't a very good attitude in my opinion. They should be prepared to pay hundreds of pounds for camp if it means that I get my Chief Scout's gold. When I go for a job I can say to the man that I may not have any qualifications but I can use an axe and saw and knife safely and I know someone who's killed a cockerel which is much more use than a GCSE in media studies or whatever else I may or may not be taking. Mummy smiled so I told her that I loved her and she told me that she loved me too so without even stopping to think I said, "Mummy, I blew the door off the microwave." She said, "I know. I was wondering how long it would take you to own up." I haven't told her about the holes in my sleeping bag, though. That one will have to wait a bit longer.

### Friday 20th March
### Alex
Things are really hotting up at Scouts now. Skip told us that we're going to be making go-karts as part of our Creative Challenge Award. Once made, we're going to have a timed race down four hundred metres of Botany Bay Lane. "Watch out for the Kid Brook at the bottom!" (which is a river) said Skip with a smile. As if!

I asked Skip tonight what James would have under his sleeping bag when he wasn't hanging off Mount Everest and he said "anything" which wasn't much help. However he did explain that all I needed was something to insulate me from the damp ground, like a groundsheet which we have in some of our tents, but not all of them apparently. I said that I had nothing on my last camp but that I had been using bubble wrap in my bedroom and he looked at me a bit puzzled and said "cool" although it's more than that, more like, "hot". Trust me to have a good idea.

Now that I'm sleeping on my bedroom floor, despite being a centimetre off the ground thanks to my duvet insulation, I can't reach my bedside lamp. I could put it on the floor next to me but that isn't very "Scout" as Tegan told me that they don't normally have electricity on any Scout camp and not just surviving camp like we've just been on. So now I need to get a torch. At the end of Scouts I asked Jimmy for his advice as he will probably have a good one now that he is an asshole. Jimmy said that he got his from China. This does seem rather a long way to go for a torch and they would also be rather expensive. I was only expecting a good one to cost a few pounds. Maybe Jimmy buys a shipload at a time. That would keep the price down. I'll ask Laura tomorrow, she'll know.

Mummy still hasn't sewn my badges back on, including my expensive new Woodpecker petrol badge onto my shirt. This evening Skip gave me a new Woodpecker badge saying that he felt sorry for me. I just hope that he doesn't tell mummy as there's no way I can send one back to the shop and get a refund for £45.39. Maybe they'll swap it for a better sleeping bag?

**Friday 20th March**

**Skip**

Joe's managed to get all his new badges sewn on but Alex still hasn't. I've given Alex another Woodpecker badge as lack of it seems to be causing him a load of grief. I texted his mum to tell her and all I got back from her was a stream of abuse along the lines of, "Now he's got two and do you know how much one of them has cost me? Forty-five pounds!" I really don't know what she's talking about and I haven't texted her back, and am not going to text her back, to find out.

**Saturday 21st March**
**Alex**

I rang Laura and told her that she should never go into Jake's bedroom and she said that she couldn't think of anything worse, then she asked why not so I told her that she might see something that would cause her to faint and she said yeah I can imagine and giggled. I like Laura. She has a nice giggle. Then I asked her how much her dad's torch from China cost and she said that it was about seven pounds. I thought that this was quite a good price so I put my order in there and then. "When's Jimmy, that's your dad, going to China next?" I asked her. "Next?" she said. "He's never been to China." "So how does he collect his torches?" "The man who makes them sells them to him, you daft twat." I'm certainly not a daft twat. Girls who giggle shouldn't call boys that like them Twats. Even if the boy in question did eat her Isambard and not tell her about it. But he wasn't the only one. If my Woodpecker badge cost forty-five pounds and that was sent from just a few miles away, then how can Laura's dad get a torch sent from China for just seven pounds when China is about ten thousand miles away? At my reckoning that should make a torch cost about seven hundred pounds. Maybe Laura got a bit confused with her decimal point. Anyway, my order's in now for a seven pound torch so she can't change the price now. Looks like I'm going to get a bargain. I rang the badge shop to see if I could swap my Woodpecker badge for a sleeping bag but didn't get very far because the line just went dead.

## Sunday 22nd March
### Alex
I told daddy at breakfast that I needed to buy a torch and that it would cost about seven hundred pounds. Daddy said that that wasn't a torch it was a sweary lighthouse. What does he know about how much things cost these days? When I was in Dover last summer, mummy saw a lighthouse for sale in an estate agent's window. She told me that it was seven hundred thousand pounds. Now who's getting their decimal points muddled up eh, daddy? However, a lighthouse is no use in my bedroom when I don't even have a torch.

## Monday 23rd March
### Skip
This evening Akela phoned. This normally means trouble and tonight was no exception. Here's how the conversation went -
Me: Hallo, er Hugo speaking.
Akela: Hallo, John. It's Leaza here. Cub camp was, I think I'll call it, er, interesting.
Me: You had nice weather.
Akela: I had the usual cuts and bruises.
Me: A bit chilly though.
Akela: The first aid kit was well-used.
Me: Did you do an Easter egg hunt?

109

Akela: John, why would I need a rectal thermometer?

Me: In case you had something in your mouth already?

Akela: And hydrogen peroxide?

Me: I don't know, you're the one with the Chemistry degree. Maybe you could bleach your hair?

Akela: I'm not accusing you, John, you understand. But I give the Cubs full responsibility to look after themselves within the confines of a first aid kit.

Me: Yes...

Akela: On Saturday night, after the Cubs had gone to bed, there was a dull green hue about one of the patrol tents. It was glowing ever so slightly. It was a particularly dark night; as you know it was a new moon on Friday.

Me: Err, yes. Of course.

Akela: I went over to investigate and called to the Cubs in the radioactive tent to turn their lights off as it was half past ten. And do you know what they said?

Me: Err, no.

Akela: They said, "We can't." Then they said, "Alfie's lost his torch and so we went and had a look in the first aid box for one of those silver reflective heat blanket things, cos you said that it can be used to reflect light in an emergency. So we went and had a look in the first aid and we found six emergency glow-in-the-dark balloons. We're sorry, Akela, we took all of them." I said, "Never mind that. What did you do with them?" "We brought them back to the tent and opened them. They all have their own little packet so they're quite sterile. We blew them up and tied them to the tent pole above us in here. The instructions said to shine a light on them for thirty seconds and then they will glow brightly for fifteen minutes and then have an after-glow for hours. It's quite nice in here. Do you want to have a look?" "I'ld be more interested in having a look at one of the balloons," I said. "Okay," they said and a minute later the tent opened and a hand thrust out what looked like an oversized rubber cucumber. "Night, night, Akela," they said and tied the tent back up. I took my cucumber back to the mess tent and walked in, still holding it in my hand. And do you know what [adult helper] said? She said, "Be prepared!" And do you know what I was holding?

There was a slight pause, as if finally expecting a reply, so, I said, "Err, no," rather too cautiously.

Akela: It was a luminous condom. A LUM – IN - OUS CON - DOM. Why ever would a Cub want a luminous condom?

Me: Emergency lighting?

Akela: No! Why were they in the first aid box?

Me: Because...

Akela: Why would my Cubs need condoms?

Me: Not necessarily the Cubs, but maybe...

Akela: No! And certainly not luminous ones. If you saw that floating around the woods in the middle of the night it would most definitely give you the...

Me: Willies?

Akela: Did you put them there?

Me: Yes.

Akela: Why?

Me: Condoms can be used as survival aids and not just for when, well, you know.

Akela: What survival?

By now I was really having to think on my feet.

Me: All sorts of situations that not necessarily Cubs, but definitely Scouts, might find themselves in. I'll put together a list. Now, do you think you could just replenish the supply seeing as you've used up all the stock? I can tell you where to get them from. Akela? Akela?

## Friday 27th March
## Alex

Go-karts are GO! Woodpeckers (plus Kestrel) are on top of this activity. Skip said that it's all about teamwork, and what a team Woodpeckers have! Josh is bringing the wood. He said that it fell off the back of a lorry, which seems to have been a bit careless. Tegan's dad is supplying all the nuts and bolts. Joe is bringing the wheels and Skip is letting us have some rope for steering. But our secret weapon is Joe's dad. He's going to help us! As a car and bike mechanic he should know a thing or two about how go-karts work. Joe says that his dad's nickname is grease monkey which is near enough to a powder monkey that is another ship's position. Joe thinks that he's going to be project manager but I DON'T THINK SO. He's only just been invented, like me. I reckon Joe's dad should be project manager. I'll ring Skip up and tell him. Anyway, Joe's just become a Woodpecker again cos Skip moved him back from Eagles. I think that the reason is that because Chloe is an atheist she is a bad influence on Joe as he keeps being sick. Mind you, Chloe hasn't been looking too well either recently. On the other hand Tegan is not an atheist cos she made the Scout Promise (the real one – no coughing) so she will look after Joe better. However he cannot be an assistant petrol leader before me as I was in Woodpeckers first even though I didn't officially recognise it. Anyway, Tegan's dad is Gunner so that must count for something. I'll ring Gunner up and tell him.

## Friday 27th March
## Skip

At least the Scouts are working together on their new project go-karts! They're going to be fairly slow (Scouts and go-karts) as they're only going down the slope that then goes over the Kyd Brook using the wide wooden bridge so no one will fall in. I've already done the risk assessment headed "Go-Karting" and, as usual, I've slipped in some extras because I'm sure no one reads them. Under "hazard identified" I've just put, "Scouts." Under "Persons at Risk" I've put, "Scouts." Under "How is the risk controlled" I've put, "I've yet to work out how to control this particular risk." Under "What further controls are needed?" I've put, "Stop sending them to Scout meetings." Under "Person responsible for controls" I've put, "No one will be in proper control." Thinking about it, that doesn't sound too good. I think I'd better do it all again. Maybe. If I've time. After all, Scouting doesn't take up much time. Just an hour a week, allegedly.

## Saturday 28th March
### Alex

I rang Hugo this morning and said to tell Skip that Joe wanted to be project manager but that I don't think he should be and that I thought that Joe's dad should be project manager and Hugo said that his dad would think about it. I then rang Tegan and told her to tell Gunner that I should be the next assistant petrol leader. She then told me that Josh had been reinstated and that no one else was going to be assistant petrol leader until she had left. This means that Josh would become petrol leader and I would be assistant petrol leader so long as Joe didn't stick his nose in. Anyway, Joe's been sick twice so I can't think that he's a more suitable assistant petrol leader than I would be. I haven't been sick once. Well not in Scouts or on camp anyway. I was sick in Cubs though when I was on camp in the tented village (which meant we didn't have to put our tents up). We had proper bunk beds with a wooden slutty

113

floor like you sometimes get at swimming pools in the changing areas so that you can get your trousers on without getting your feet too wet cos the water runs between the sluts. But I was only sick cos I drank a whole bottle of double concentrate orange squash for a dare when we were in the tent and supposed to be asleep. It probably didn't help that I had eaten beef stew and apple pie and custard for tea and then four doughnuts in bed and a packet of Haribos and a Creme Egg. I was in the top bunk and didn't have time to warn Stanley who was beneath me. At least I missed his bed. His new hiking boots weren't so lucky though. He had put them next to him on the floor in case someone stole them. Well, no one was going to steal them after I had filled them up with sick. The rest of it went between the sluts and disappeared. However, in the morning I felt much better so we didn't tell Akela but the tent stank so it had to be Lynx Africad. We used a whole can that Stanley had borrowed from his brother without telling him. Stanley washed his boots out then they were all wet inside so he told Akela that he had left them outside in the rain and they had got wet. Akela told him that it hadn't rained and then someone suggested that he had weed in them in the night. He never told on me. Stanley couldn't go on the hike and had to stay behind in the tent. Then he was sick, which wasn't surprising seeing as he was sitting on top of a sewer, so he then had to go home. He left Cubs after that and we never saw him again. He's probably grown out of his hiking boots and they'll be upstairs in the Scout Hut waiting for someone to borrow. Can you imagine putting your feet into boots that someone's been sick in and then it's dried up? When the next person goes on a hike and starts getting sweaty feet it will do something like melt or something in the insides of the boots and then they'll start to pong all over again.

114

**Saturday 28th March**
**Skip**
Spent half an hour this morning sorting out project managers for the go-karting activity. Hugo said that Alex had 'phoned and suggested that Tegan be the Woodpecker's project manager. This was actually a great suggestion so I've put her down. Then Tegan rang Hugo and asked if Josh could be reinstated as APL which I will do as he's had enough punishment and he's coming along quite nicely now.

**Wednesday 1st April**
**Alex**
Skip rang mummy and told her to tell me that he's decided that Tegan can be the Woodpecker's project manager. That's stupid. She's a girl. I thought Skip would ring back later and say "April Fool" but he didn't. Tegan won't be able to lead by example. She won't be able to use a saw. It's just as well we've done our emergency aid badge. She'll need all that expertise when she saws her finger off. Anyway I rang Tegan and told her that if Josh was assistant petrol leader and stayed there until she left, then she could become a senior petrol leader with three stripes then I could become petrol leader. Then we would be the dream team. Tegan and me that is, not Josh. She said that it was not her decision but as her dad is Gunner she will have some influence. I didn't mention that I knew that she was project manager.

**Friday 3rd April**
**Alex**
Joe's dad was very impressed with the Woodpeckers' work this evening. He told us that we were very productive

(unlike some of the petrols mentioning no names, ahem Eagles). We were organised, efficient and focussed. That's what he said. We were shown how to use a saw properly, again, for the benefit of those who hadn't been paying attention last month, cutting on the down stroke. Tegan sawed the mainframe and axle and still has all her fingers. Josh brought in some forbatoo. Tegan sawed it into two bits. Joe and Josh couldn't manage the sawing. I could have done had I had a go, which I didn't as I was busy elsewhere. I had learnt how to saw last month and on the camp but I thought I would let Tegan have a go. We bolted the axle to the mainframe and then we attached an old chair, minus the legs, for the driver to sit in. We finished with the wheels and the rope so that we had something to hold onto. I then popped my new torch on the front and secured it with a bit of blue tack. Daddy had relented, that's what he said, and bought me a really big torch, far better than Skip's even. I'll have to be careful in case he tries to steal it. We were so quick that we had time for Joe's dad to make a wooden box to put behind the seat. He said that it was like a glove compartment in a car. It's a bit odd that in daddy's car gloves are about the only things that don't go into the glove compartment. Never mind, I'll bring some. Joe's dad decided that, for the race, we wouldn't be called Woodpeckers but Team Frari.

**Friday 3rd April**
**Skip**
Group Scout Leader has rung to say that she's seen the risk assessment for the go-karts and "some of it is a bit flippant." I told her that I approach all risk assessments with care, professionalism and passion and that nothing will go wrong because all corners of the square are covered. Well, a three

sided square maybe.

## Saturday 4th April
## Alex
Our house has a doorbell so my bedroom needs one too. I went out today and bought a remote controlled one for just five pounds. It has a number of different rings but the one that I have settled on is a dog barking. That will keep unwanted people out of my bedroom. I've stuck the button bit on our front door next to the ding-dong one and the woofey bit in my tent. It works a treat! Unwanted visitors are warned! KEEP OUT! DOGS! Woof, woof!

## Friday 10th April
## Alex
Frari night! I found out tonight from Josh that Joe had got into a bit of trouble during the week. His brother had gone to get his bicycle out from the garage and then had gone complaining to his mummy that the wheels had gone missing and all he was left with was the frame. It was unfortunate that Joe's daddy had taken the go-kart home to "polish it up a bit." Joe's mummy looked under a sheet in the garage and found the wheels on our Team Frari go-kart. Joe pleaded with her to let them stay on until the end of the race and so she relented. That's two people who have relented this week. Just as well. A go-kart with no back wheels could have been interesting – and slow. As it turned out Woodpeckers would probably have won even without any wheels at all.

Joe's dad wheeled our Frari into the Scout Hut. It looked rather oily but Joe's dad said that he had been "seeing to the wheels" which I thought meant making sure that they were

117

well screwed on to stop Joe's brother from taking them back before we were ready. Joe's daddy had made the glove box much bigger. He said that this was because we would want to store our drinks in there if we were going on a long journey. Another good idea. Whenever I go on camp I have to take a water bottle in case I get thirsty so I have to put water in it. Then it gets too heavy to carry. I bet when James goes on a journey he travels light. Fat chance with a big bottle of water. What I need is a water bottle on wheels, a bit like having a dog on a lead but a bottle of water instead. Joe's dad said that he had added a "secret part" to the go-kart. I thought that this probably meant loads of grease or some narrower wheels. He's clever like that. He had added some extra wood all around and it was beginning to look more like a car than a kart. He had also boxed in the axle, saying that he wanted to keep it safe from "little fingers". Josh said that his daddy had a friend called "Little Fingers". Probably not the same person though. I asked Josh if his dad had ever been a Scout. He said that he hadn't but he had been a "tea leaf". Josh is very odd. And his daddy must keep some very strange company – when he's not in prison that is. I don't expect that his tea-leaf friend has ever been in jail, more like a mental hospital with a name like that. I don't think that Josh should ever be petrol leader. Mind you he's not ever going to be if I am first.

Once Skip had given the four go-karts a quick "once over" he told us to take them to the top of Botany Bay Lane where we would regroup. This was going to be fun. We were all very excited. Four hundred metres of a sloping country track that was nearly as steep as Old Hill but without the parked cars and motorists that can't drive and "watch out for the Kid Brook at the bottom!" we all screamed together as Skip reminded us once more.

We were a bit late starting as Skip said that Eagles had decided to make their go-kart out of a dinghy trailer that they had found upstairs in the Scout Hut. This could have been a good idea with a ready-made main frame and axle, Joe's dad said, however...! Eagles decided to make the axle much wider so that it could fit all of them on it so that they could all go down Botany Bay Lane together. This did seem a bit stupid as more weight would mean slower. Anyway, that wasn't the main problem. The main problem was that they had made the axle too wide and so couldn't get their go-kart out of the Scout Hut door. Now who are twats? It took them some minutes to work out that if they turned their go-kart on its side then it would fit through the door – just.

[Botany Bay Lane is a single-track lane in Chislehurst that winds its way down to a farm where the lane ends and a track starts that goes down to Kyd Brook, over a wooden bridge and up to meet the railway line. The one-bar gate at the start of the track was no barrier to Scout go-karts, so long as they kept their heads down.]

Eagles went first. (No lights!) They pointed their go-kart down the hill and then the five of them jumped on. And then? Nothing! At least nothing to start with. Then nothing to finish with. There was a squeal (times five), the frame sagged, the wheels splayed out like a foal trying to walk, Skip said. Eagles weren't going anywhere. And that meant they weren't going to win anything. Gunner was at the bottom of the hill and he walkie-talkied Skip to ask him when to start the stopwatch. Skip said, "The Eagles have landed," and Gunner cackled over the walkie-talkie. I don't know why this was so funny. They hadn't even taken off.

Next it was Hawks. Their go-kart was a bit more normal, although it wasn't going to win - and didn't. Jake, who is their petrol leader, had used some wheels from a shopping trolley because he said he couldn't find any others. Jake jumped into the seat, Skip blew his whistle and Gunner started the stopwatch. And then stopped it. Jake's shopping-trolley-go-kart was completely unable to be steered. It started off down the lane and then swerved violently into the hedge at the side. There was a short delay whilst Skip had to extract Jake from the hedge. Then it was Raven's turn.

After Woodpeckers, Ravens are the most competent. Hugo is their petrol leader and he knows what he's doing. He jumped on their go-kart, the whistle blew, the stopwatch started and Hugo disappeared into the darkness. A short while later we heard Gunner's whistle and the walkie-talkie crackled. "One minute, fifty eight seconds," said Gunner. This was quite a good time but we were going to beat it. Well, we had to beat it as the other two petrols had no time to beat. At this point the Scouts at the top of the lane thought that it would be more fun to go and wait at the bottom to cheer / jeer Woodpeckers' go-kart. They all trudged down the hill leaving yours truly with Joe (driver) and Joe's dad, who had been given the whistle. I adjusted the torch and then Joe's dad said to me that I was to "keep mum" as Joe jumped on the seat and PUT A CRASH HELMET ON! "How fast do you think we're going to go?" I asked. "Faster than the Ravens," was his reply as Joe's dad took the top off the glove box to reveal his "little secret."

There wasn't a water bottle to be seen anywhere. No wonder Joe's dad had been looking so shifty. He pulled a cord, there was a huge roar and Joe flew off (like an Eagle) down the track. Joe's dad said that Joe should be down in under a minute. Judging by the amount of whistle-blowing going on down in the darkness, I reckoned that Joe had already arrived. "Does it have brakes?" I asked Joe's dad, but he just laughed. We ran down the hill and at the bottom where the track crosses over the brook it was chaos. The other Scouts were screaming with laughter. Skip, who was actually standing in the brook, was trying to explain that to avoid hitting them, as they had no idea what was coming and were standing across the track where it levelled out, Joe had had to take evasive action and in doing so had swerved then jumped off the kart just as the kart launched itself over the side of the wooden bridge and into the Kid Brook. Joe kept going then fell into the brook on the other side of the bridge. Skip hauled Joe out first, followed by our go-kart. "Not bad," said Skip with a smile. "Forty-eight seconds" said Gunner. "Does that mean we've won?" Joe spluttered. "Not with a four-stroke engine helping you," said Skip. "Disqualified."

I don't think Joe's brother's going to get much of his bicycle back. And one of Joe's dad's customers is going to be having a few words about his engine-less motorbike.

As we started to trudge up the hill, Joe said that he could see a strange bright light bobbing up and down in the brook as it disappeared off on its course down to Mottingham. "That's not a strange light," I cried. "It's my seven hundred pound torch." But no one was interested.

**Friday 10th April**

## Skip

Fantastic evening at Scouts tonight with life, laughter, spills and thrills. Joe's dad did us proud. Gosh, if the Ferrari had gone any faster we could have had a 21st Century equivalent of Chitty Chitty Bang Bang on our hands. As it turned out it was more like Herbie Rides Again. Still, I'm showing my age. I'd better just tweak the risk assessment before I go to bed. Trouble is, I can't find it.

## Saturday 11th April
## Skip

'Phone call from Group Scout Leader asking if go-karting went alright. Told her it was fine and that no one was killed. Thought I had better get that in first. "Did anyone end up in the Kyd Brook?" she asked. "Errrr, yes. But they were looking for Alex's torch." Phew, that was a close shave. I must have a traitor in the camp. How am I going to find out who it is?

## Friday 17th April
## Alex

No Scouts tonight as it's Easter. However I still have my Scout hat on. Unfortunately I am in the dog house today as our house wasn't cleaned. Sheila came to do her weekly clean but she's not very good with animals. She phoned mummy this afternoon and told her that when she came round this morning she rang the doorbell then freaked out because she could hear a pack of Alsatians upstairs. She dropped all her cleaning stuff on the drive and ran back home. She wasn't ever a Scout, that's for sure.

## Saturday 18th April
## Skip

We've had a day clearing up the Scout Hut and the grounds today. We've filled a black sack full of lost property that I said that I would take to the charity shop. The hut is looking clearer and cleaner than it has for ages.

We've finally got agreement from [the landlords] that we can level the slope to the side to enable more camping to take place at the hut. This involves digging out the top bit and depositing it on the bottom bit. In the process Aaron dug up what I think one would call a "suspect device." There was a lot of squeaking and squealing so, to calm the Scouts down, I put it in the wheelbarrow and parked it round the side by the footpath. Later on I wheeled it home. On the way a thought struck me. What if it actually is a bomb? I figured that if it was and it blew up then at least I wouldn't know much about it. It's now sitting on the drive whilst I get round to searching the internet to find out what it is.

## Saturday 18th April
**Alex**

Matthew and I had to go to the Scout Hut today to clear up. Mummy and daddy were supposed to come cos all children needed an adult but mum said it would be alright and no one would notice. When we arrived everyone was very busy in the outside area. Skip came up and said hi and asked where mummy and daddy were and I said oh, they're just coming. We had brought a spade between the two of us and then Skip said that we were going to be digging earth not building sand-castles. We put the spade down once Skip disappeared and we went round the back to play football where no one would find us. Then there was a lot of excitement cos Aaron dug up a bomb from the Second World War and even Gunner didn't know what type it was even though I think he was in the war. Aaron picked it up and said that it wasn't ticking which was okay then cos all bombs tick just before they go off according to Aaron. The digging was going to take forever so I suggested to Skip that if we put the bomb on the top of the slope and give it a kick and then if it blows up it would be much easier for the levelling. Skip then asked who should forfeit their legs if not their life for a few hours digging and I said, well I didn't know who to suggest so I said we could just throw a brick at it but Skip said no. Then Skip put it in a wheelbarrow and moved it out of the way and said that he was going to take it home. Maybe he wants some earth moving in his garden so he's going to give it a kick when he gets home. After that we went home after we had had some squash and some cake.

## Sunday 19th April
### Skip
I drove past [Scout camp site] this morning and it was buzzing with a large gathering of some description going on. Then I remembered that I had the bag of lost property in the back of the car and before I had managed to stop myself I had driven into the car park, taken out the black sack and wandered round the camp site strategically dropping t-shirts, forks cups, trousers, (even the Maid of Honour knickers) near the tents and, in the case of those that weren't done up, actually in the tents. I love the idea of no longer having lost property when we can now have "found property." I just hope Maid of Honour didn't end up in one of the boys' tents. That would be difficult for little Johnnie to explain when he got home and his mum tipped his washing out. Soon I was on my way, avoiding someone by the building who shouted out, "Can I help you?" I just waved cheerily and called back, "Just doing a site recce for a couple

of weeks' time." With an acknowledging smile and a thumb in the air I was soon on my way.

## Thursday 23rd April
### Alex
Today is Saint George's Day. Saint George is the patron saint of Scouting and that means that we have to honour him on Sunday.

## Friday 24th April
### Skip
Tonight the Scouts had a talk about survival and how to make do with common objects. I was going to spend an evening on how to light a fire using anything but matches but, whilst playing a game with balloons, I had a better idea. Akela was still owed an explanation as to why she, or more accurately the Cubs, had come across a load of condoms in the first aid. I sat the Scouts down in a large circle and gave them a balloon each. "Now I know that you can blow these up and use them as decorations, but what else could they be used for in a survival situation?" The first suggestion was as water carriers. If you have nothing else, balloons make very good water carriers. Then someone suggested that, seeing as we were going to be talking about fires, they would be very useful for keeping tinder in where it would remain very dry. Another Scout suggested that they could be used as the rubbery bits in catapults for shooting for our food. Tegan suggested that we could use them as surgical gloves, probably more accurate to call it a mitten, if we cut the end off. Then Josh said that we could blow it up and paint a face on it and it could become our friend. When I told him not to be so silly, he told me that it was important to have a friend in a survival situation. "Tom Hanks had a friend in Cast

Away. It was a volleyball with a face on it that he talked to."
So that was five ideas for me to give to Akela. Then Josh
added, "I've just thought of another one. You could use it as
a condom if you wanted to have sex." It was time to move
onto fire lighting and the beetle drive preparation.

**Friday 24th April**
**Alex**
This evening we did a bit more of survival and fire lighting.
Josh said that he wanted to have sex, but I wasn't really
listening. Akela is organising a Beetle Drive for next month
for all sections, including parents, in 3rd Chislehurst. Skip
has decided that we should have a practice run so that the
Scout section at least will know what to do. You have to
draw a beetle in bits and which bits you draw are decided on
by the number that you throw on a dice with a six to start.
After someone shouts "beetle" the Scout with the fewest
beetle parts drawn on each table goes backwards to the
previous table, and if you score the most points on your
table, then you move up one table. If you score "beetle" first
you score fourteen points: one for his body, one for his head,
two for his eyes, two for his feelers, six for his legs and two
for his wings. We had only been going for about a minute
when Barnaby shouted "Beetle!" I had only just thrown a
six. Barnaby moved up a table and I was the one to move
down. Then we started game two. Once more, Barnaby
shouted "beetle" after a minute. Everyone sighed and
Barnaby beamed. When it happened again in the third
round Skip marched over to Barnaby's table and picked up
his piece of paper. "And what's the meaning of this?" asked
Skip in his firm voice which he uses quite a lot, looking at
Barnaby with a very cross expression. Skip then drew
Barnaby's latest beetle on the whiteboard. He then said,

"let's count all the body parts, shall we? One, two, three....
So Barnaby, the beetles are supposed to have fourteen body
parts, so why does your one only have three?" Barnaby
explained that his beetle has a body but only has one leg
instead of six because, "one was eaten by a rat when the
beetle was sleeping, one came off in a fight, one sizzled off
when it flew too close to a bonfire, one broke off in a skiing
accident and one was chopped off in an argument with a
chainsaw. It has a head but no eyes because it was blinded
as a child and so the eyes don't count. It had two feelers but
one day it was 'feeling' too close to a mad dog who took
revenge, and its wings melted when it flew too close to the
sun. So, Skip, I only need to throw one six, one five and one
three." Then he added, before Skip could say anything, "Are
you going to discriminate against my beetle because it's
disabled?" Skip said that he was discriminating against
Barnaby because he was a cheat at which point Barnaby
burst into tears and the game was cancelled. But we got the
idea of how to play and loads of Scouts signed up. It should
be fun!

After all that excitement we all needed a stiff drink which is
what mummy calls them. I think it means a drink with lots
of gin. Skip had brought in a cocktail shaker and we ordered
our drinks from a list and measured out the ingredients and
then mixed them in a cup and then Skip shook them in his
shaker. I had a Tequila Sunrise which was very yummy.
When mummy picked me up I told her that I had a bit of a
head which is what mummy often says at breakfast time. I
told her that I had been drinking cocktails. She tried to
speak to Skip but there were other parents lined up so we
came home.

**Saturday 25th April**
**Skip**
I looked out of the bedroom window this morning and thought that I really must do something about the rusty bomb in a wheelbarrow. All week I had tried to find something that resembled it on the internet but to no avail. Reminds me of when I was having a conservatory built at the cottage. Billy [the builder] said that Webbo [the labourer] was taking the bullets home. "What bullets?" "The ones he dug up." Webbo had dug up half a dozen .303 bullets from World War I or II. I knew what they were because I had used them in the army cadets at school when I were a lad, in Lee-Enfield rifles that we used to charge around the Kent countryside letting off at every opportunity. Designed to polish off humans, they used to make quite nice holes in rabbits. He showed me where he had found them, about a foot below ground and, after a bit of scraping we found a load more, in total over fifty. I told him, "Webbo, these three inch chaps pack quite a punch, as my old school friend xxxxx will tell you. He's just about still with us to tell the tale after he took one home from school and thereupon met with a life-changing injury that involved said bullet, a vice, a hammer and a nail. Look, they're even starting to sweat; I'll call the police." The police were called and once they ascertained that they were over fifty years old they advised me to ring the Royal Artillery Barracks at Woolwich Arsenal and gave me the 'phone number. I dialled the number and was met with a "Blenkington-Smyth." It was all I could do to get "Hemming-Clark" out, but I managed. It was if we were communicating through surnames. "Jolly good, jolly good. What can I do for you Hemming-Clark?" I assumed a General manner of speaking. "Now look here. I've been advised to give you a call because

128

down here in Chislehurst one of my men has unearthed a cache of .303 bullets from way-back when. They're a bit sweaty and I don't want them to go off unexpectedly and finish off the bulldog." "Nothing to worry about, old chap. Not our bag really. A bit to small. We like to play with things you can't lift by hand. I'll get a Panda round. Good day." And with that he was gone. In due course a Panda and PC turned up. "I've been told to come and pick up some bullets." "What are you going to put them in?" "A specimen bag? Will that do?" "I would have thought a lead lined box would have been safer but that's up to you. At the very least put them in the boot." The PC gathered up the bullets, put them in the back of the Panda next to a petrol can and drove off. I was mightily relieved when after ten minutes had passed I still hadn't heard any loud CRACKs and witnessed a blood-stained PC staggering up my drive, clutching his arm and calling for an ambulance.

Fortunately nowadays arms are dealt with a little bit more professionally. During the week a fellow Scout leader called Pike, so named for his Gypsy heritage or his love of fishing – I don't know which, I'll ask him some day - said that if it gets as far as Bomb Disposal they'll blow the device up anyway, whatever it is, so I put the wheelbarrow next to my car and phoned 101. Despite this being the non-emergency number, within ten minutes I had six police officers staring at my bomb in the wheelbarrow. "We'll take a photo, ping it over to explosives, and if they don't know what it is they pop over. In the meantime, stay indoors. But don't worry, explosives always know what they're dealing with from a picture." Two minutes later the road was cordoned off and one of the police officers was on my doorstep. "Explosives don't know what it is and they're coming over. Stay indoors and away from the windows." "How long will they be?" "Not long." Yeah sure! Actually, they weren't long. Goodness knows where they had been waiting but no more than five minutes later I had a fully padded out explosives' officer, with patches and things on her clothing that I couldn't even identify, peering into the wheelbarrow. "It's okay. It's not going to explode."

Me: So it's not a bomb?

Explosives Officer: No. It's a gas cartridge from an old fire extinguisher.

Me: So you'll be blowing it up so that I can get a new wheelbarrow?

Explosives Officer: Is that why you wheeled the device home, so that you could position it next to your car?

Me: Err, possibly.

Explosives Officer: Insurance doesn't normally cover bomb explosions.

Me: Please don't blow it up.

Explosives Officer: I'm minded to now, but we're just going to take it away and dispose of it as scrap.

Me: Can I keep it to play "Pass the Bomb" with the Scouts?

Explosives Officer: No.

Doesn't stop me from telling the Scouts that it was a bomb though.

## Sunday 26th April
### Alex

Today is St George's Day parade. The Cubs made a St George and the Beavers made dragons and we paraded down Chislehurst High Street for a service in a field. Marculf is from Georgia which I think's in America. He's not all there with learning our language yet. He's just started in

Scouts. He's a Raven. He told me that the Beavers had made a horse. I had to explain that St George was a horse that breathed fire and that the Beavers were making a dragon. Marculf's going to have to learn a lot more facts about the Scouts if he wants to be Chief Scout (not that he's going to be). He told me that St George is patron saint of Georgia. Shows how much he knows. Everyone knows that there are no saints in America as it has a president. We had to renew our Scout Promise. Chloe renewed her Scout Promise even though she is an atheist. She didn't cough this time. She even had to say a prayer. Well, she didn't have to but Skip had asked for volunteers and only Chloe did. She was supposed to say a prayer for all the Scout leaders in the world, but she said, "We pray for Skip, Hugo's dad, who is the best Scout leader in the world. Amen." There were some important people there in suits. Our MP was there. That's a member of parliament which is important. Skip told me who he was. He's not an atheist as he's an MP. He wasn't wearing a suit, he had a jacket on so he's probably more important than maybe he thinks. Skip didn't know who the other people were apart from the Scout people. I didn't know either but they all had suits on so were probably less important than they thought. I could have asked them but we weren't allowed to talk to them but we had to walk past them at the end while we were doing the Scout salute. Our MP smiled at me as we did the march past. Maybe he would prefer to be a Scout leader. I bet Scout leaders get paid more. Skip made a rude gesture to one of the Scout leaders who was wearing loads of badges and he shouted something back. He sounded quite cross and I thought that there may be a punch-up but then he smiled so there wasn't.

**Friday 1st May**

## Alex

Today is May Day. We have a day off from school on Monday. Marculf told me that today is St Marculf's Day so I did "pinch and a punch" on him. I don't think he understood. I think he's being stupid. I asked him when St Alex's Day is and he said that he would find out. Twat.

Last year at Rotary Summer Fair the Cubs and Scouts had stall. The Scouts made a bagatelle board out of a sheet of forbyate. It wasn't very good though. We made an edge and used nails for pockets and golf balls for balls. The highest score won a prize. The highest score was five hundred when I went for my break but when I got back I found that Lee had put a new name on the board, someone called Spencer who had scored one thousand, two hundred. Then Lee said that the man had had three goes but only paid for one cos he had said that one pound was too much for just one go then he added all his three scores together and doubled it and that's what you do in bagatelle and Lee was scared of him so said OK and put his score on the board and at the end of the day he won the prize. And when Skip found out he was very cross but didn't do anything cos his name was on the board.

This year the Scouts are going to make an even bigger one. Skip's bought TWO sheets of forbyate and tonight we had to paint it. We decided to paint it in 3rd Chislehurst colours, i.e. black and red. Cos black is the main colour on our scarves and red round the outside we were going to paint it that way round but we thought it would be a bit depressing with all that black so we did it the other way round so we had loads of black paint left over and we ran out of red cos we had to do several coats. First of all we had to put the two sheets of forbyate on tables to make it easier to paint. Then we had to use primer and undercoat and topcoat. Skip says that primer helps the main paint to stick and undercoat fills in the little holes in the wood. Then he said that he had bought a paint that was both primer and undercoat in one so we don't need two different types of paint. Maybe it should just be called primecoat or something. That dried really quickly so then we had to paint the edges black and forbyate red. Skip gave Tegan's team one pot of 750g of red paint and said that it should last for three coats, but it didn't. It lasted one coat and then it ran out so the other sheet of forbyate stayed white. Skip then looked at it and said that it looked like nasty colours but it looks okay to me. I think it looks quite lively.

**Friday 1st May**
**Skip**
This evening we started work on The World's Largest Bagatelle Board. I contact the Guinness people and we've applied for it to be recognised as such. With two sheets of four by eight foot hardboard stuck together end to end we should be record breakers. When I went and got the paint from B & Q I told the guy that I wanted the brightest red that they had. I told him what it was for and he said that he was sorry but it was water-based and not oil-based. Given that it was going to be the Scouts that were going to be using it, this is probably just as well.

The evening went very well and without a hitch. The Scouts all wore disposable aprons and gloves, but this didn't prevent them from painting themselves as well as the board. They decided to change the colours round but when we had finished I told them that it looks like Nazi colours but they didn't seem too concerned. I'm not sure where all the red paint went. It was meant to do about three sheets of four by eight but we seem to have run out. I'll get some more during the week and finish it off myself.

**Friday 8th May**
**Alex**
Tonight mummy had to help at Scouts cos there was no other adult apart from Skip. I think she enjoyed herself. Skip always needs adults to help him. I think that this is because he's not safe on his own. He's always asking for help but mummy always says that there's always someone else who will help. Well, if everyone thought that then there would be no one would there mummy?

We played a great game called "Pass the Pulse." We had to make two teams and sit either side of some tables that we stuck together (not with glue or anything, just pushed together) so that we had two long lines. Then the teams had to hold hands. Skip flicked a coin at one end and the two Scouts at Skip's end had to see if it was a heads or tails. If it was a heads then the two Scouts had to squeeze the Scout's hand they were holding and pass the pulse down to the other end where there was a sweet waiting. The first Scout to grab the sweet at the other end was the winner unless the coin was a tails in which case there should have been no pulse. After each go we moved up a place so that everyone got a go at winning a sweet. I won! I didn't wait for the pulse to come (or not). I just grabbed the sweet and fortunately it was a heads so I won and wasn't disqualified. And it was chocolate.

Marculf told me tonight at Scouts that St Alex's Day is on 18th March, which I've missed. Marculf said that he was meant to have been eaten by wild animals but they didn't because they didn't like the taste of him. I looked at him a bit weird and he said not you, SAINT Alex. You're not a saint. I thought we were all saints if we made the Scout Promise. When I got home I looked up on Google "We're all saints" but all I got was a load of stuff about an English-Canadian girl group from years ago. Anyway, I don't know how Marculf knows all this as St Alex must have died before he was born.

We're going to be doing some work on the Skills Challenge Award next Friday and Skip has asked us to do some research so that we can explain the dangers and harmful effects of smoking, alcohol and drugs.

**Friday 8th May**
**Skip**
A rather calm Scout meeting tonight, thank goodness, with some sitting down games. We played "Pass the Pulse" which is always a favourite. Alex's mum came to help which was a bit of a novelty. At one point I caught Alex holding his mum's hand. It was so sweet. Alex so wants to be grown up but he's really only a child. I said to him whilst we were having squash and biscuits that it was really sweet that he could still hold his mother's hand. He pulled it away quickly and then said that he was playing "Pass the Pulse" with her. I hope she gave him her biscuit.

**Sunday 10th May**
**Alex**
I've been doing my research on the harmful effects of smoking, alcohol and drugs but this seems all a little bit one-sided so I'm going to research ALL the effects of

smoking, alcohol and drugs, especially the good bits.

**Friday 15th May**
**Skip**
We started the Skills Challenge Award this evening. I asked
the Scouts to talk about what they had found out about the
harmful effects of smoking, alcohol and drugs. Alex said
that it was a bit one-sided so he was going to give the
beneficial effects. I asked him what the beneficial effects of
smoking were. "Well, I couldn't find many, Skip. But one is
that you're less likely to have knee-replacement surgery."
"Yeah," said Tegan, "But that's only cos people who smoke
don't go running or jogging and wear their knees out."
"Okay, Tegan," I said. You seem to have quite a long list in
your hand. What are the harmful effects?" "Well, Skip,
smoking leads to mood stimulation, poor vision, anxiety and
irritability, more colds and flu, lung cancer, constricted
blood vessels, high cholesterol, heart disease, stained teeth,
smelly hair and clothes, diabetes complications, early
menopause, problems with pregnancy, problems for babies,
appetite suppression, coughing, chronic obstructive
pulmonary diseases, bronchitis, too much clotting, blood
cancer, yellow fingers, wrinkly skin, bad teeth, infertility,
cancer connection, cervical cancer and erectile dysfunction."
"Wow," I said, "that's quite a list. All to avoid a bit of knee
surgery. Any questions?" Josh put his hand up. "Please,
Skip, what is 'erectile dysfunction?'" I should have seen that
one coming. I was going to say, "Ask Tegan" but instead
said, "Well, err, it means that you can't have children." At
that, Alex piped up, "Well I would have thought that that
was an advantage."

"Let's move on to alcohol," I suggested. "Tegan, again."

"Please, Skip. Drinking too much can lead to cancers of the mouth, throat and breast, stroke, heart disease, liver disease, brain damage and damage to the nervous system." "Again, quite a list. But you did mention 'drinking too much.' Can a moderate amount of alcohol have any beneficial effects?" "Yes," said Alex without being specifically asked. "It can make you brainier. I found out that 'if you sip smart, a little tipple can help prevent cognitive decline. Researchers from Loyola University found that moderate drinkers were 23 percent less likely to develop cognitive impairment, Alzheimer's disease, and other forms of dementia compared to non-drinkers.' So there."

"Thank you, Alex. Finally, drugs. We're not talking the stuff you find in tea and coffee. We're thinking about the illegal stuff. Now then, the most well-known illegal drug is cannabis. It also has a more common name though. Does anybody know what that is?" "Please, Skip," said Josh, "I think it's called weeeeed." "Well, yes, Josh, That is one name for it. In fact it has loads of names, but I was looking for 'marijuana,' but it is also called 'weed'. Next, does anybody know what the harmful effects of taking illegal drugs can be? No one? Okay, just Tegan then. Tegan." "Please Skip, Cannabis can be smoked or eaten, often in cakes. I also found out that 'Cannabis has been linked to mental health problems such as schizophrenia and, when smoked, to lung diseases including asthma. It affects how your brain works, so regular use can make concentration and learning very difficult. Frequent use can have a negative effect on your fertility. It is also dangerous to drive after taking cannabis. Mixing it with tobacco is likely to increase the risk of heart disease and lung cancer.'" "Thank you, Tegan. Now Alex, any advantages?" "Yes, Skip. People who smoke weeeeed are likelier to be skinnier." He then added, "So I don't think Nathan's been taking any recently." "Thank you for your input, Alex, but that last comment was quite unnecessary."

## Saturday 16th May
## Alex

Today was Scout Community Week. Should be named Scout Community Day. This is when we do something to help the community rather than wrecking it. In the old days there was something called bob-a-job week. Skip said this is where you went and did jobs for people and they paid you a bob and then the Scouts spent it. Skip said that a bob was old money and that it was worth the same as five pence. This sounds a bit mean if you have to do a big job. Now we do bob-a-job as a group. This means that we can get a really big job done. Today we went clearing undergrowth at Scadbury Park. This is owned by the council. The council is very rich but it doesn't spend any money looking after this park, which is actually a woods, so we have to do it. We spent all day with spades and rakes and clippers and things. We cut some footpaths that had disappeared. Josh was on poo patrol. Everyone wanted to be on poo patrol so we had to do rock, paper, scissors for it amongst us all which took about twenty minutes. I had to do it against Josh and he beat me. He always does rock so I did paper but when I showed paper he had done scissors so I lost. He had a black sack and a stick with a pincher thing at the end to pick up poo. Hugo's mum helped. Her name is Julia. She doesn't have a proper name like Crusher. She's in charge of Scadbury Park Scout helpers. She told me that she has an invested interest in the Park as it's on her doorstep, which it's not. She lives half a mile away. I don't know what she's invested cos she's not a

Scout leader cos she told Hugo she hates camping. Mind you, I think that there are other Scout leaders that hate Scouting. Joe told me that when he was a Cub wherever he was before he came to 3rd Chislehurst they went on camp once and Akela who was supposed to be in charge went home during camp. He had a friend called Ryan who was sick in the night and Joe woke up, well you would do if someone had been sick over you. Joe said he went to wake Akela up and was calling outside her tent but there was no reply and he called and called and then he shook her tent till it nearly collapsed even though it was a Force 10 tent but there was no reply and then Trevor appeared who was an adult helper, he came out of his tent and he didn't have first aid or anything he was just an adult. Joe said that Akela wouldn't wake up and Trevor said that it was okay he would sort out the problem and Joe said that maybe Akela was dead and Trevor should check and Trevor said he would later. Then Joe said that maybe Akela had gone home cos she never really liked camping and maybe Trevor should try and ring her at home and Trevor said not to worry, she'll be around somewhere. He didn't seem very bothered. I would be bothered if I was an adult helper and I lost Akela, that's for sure. Joe said that he did suggest to Trevor that if Trevor gave Joe his phone then he would call Akela and see if she was okay but Trevor just said, "Leave it kiddo," so Joe did but he said he wasn't very happy about it.

Then Trevor asked Joe what the matter was and Joe said that Ryan had been sick and that they weren't allowed to clear it up cos they were only Cubs which wasn't true but Trevor didn't know that. Trevor said that Joe could go in the sick tent and sleep and Ryan could stay in his tent and make that the sick tent but Joe said that Trevor still had to clear

139

the sick up so he did. He had to boil up some water and take all Ryan's gear out and wash the ground sheet and then dry it and then put Ryan back and then he had to go back to bed all in the middle of the night. In the morning when Joe got up Akela was making breakfast all bright and smiley and Joe said to her that she must have been really asleep as he couldn't wake her up and he was sorry cos he tried and Trevor woke up instead and Akela said that no she was really awake and could hear all that was going on and she just didn't want to get up when Trevor was so capable of sorting out the situation. This is wrong cos she didn't know what the situation was until Trevor had got up. So Joe reckons she went home which is illegal on camp. Anyway she was all whistley and happy all camp and Joe reckons that the only reason would be that she had had a really good night's sleep. She might've had ear plugs in though I reckon, cos you can get them if you do a noisy job, probably being a Scout leader counts but it's a bit silly having them in at night if you're supposed to be listening for people being sick and stuff like that. I bet if you could invent some ear plugs that would stop you hearing Scout chattering but would still allow you to hear Scout noises like someone being sick or being murdered then you could make a fortune.

When people walk their dogs and the dog has a poo, some people just leave it which is disgusting. Other people pick it up and put it in a little bag and then throw it in the undergrowth. This is disgusting too and a bit odd. Why would anyone bother picking up their dog's poo and then throw it away once it's in a little bag? They could at least take it home with them. Josh found fifty-three bags of poo in the undergrowth. Hugo's mum took a picture of them. She must have some very strange photos on her phone. Josh said that when she's with her friends and they're all looking at their photos, Hugo's mum will say, "Oh here's a really good one that I took. It's a picture of fifty-three bags of dog poo that I collected in Scadbury Park," and all her friends will say, "Cool" cos that's what mummies say to each other. Hugo's mum said that the work that we were doing was a great benefit for those who use the park as they could now walk easier and safer with their dogs or babies. Then Marculf told Hugo's mum that he wanted a baby. I told Marculf that he couldn't have a baby if he had a reptile dysfunction. When Hugo's mum told him that he should wait until he was married he said that Chloe hadn't waited. He said that Chloe had a baby and she wasn't married. Hugo's mum just smiled at him and said, "I hope not." I hope not too. I like Chloe. I hope she's not married.

On the way out of the park Josh was sick. Josh said it was cos of the thought of all the poo that he had collected up. Skip then made him pick up all the little bits of sick with his little pincher stick thing. Hugo's mum didn't take a picture though, thank goodness. Skip said that it was good practice and if Josh managed it he would be okay in a Chinese restaurant with chop sticks when it came to picking up rice.

**Friday 22nd May**
**Alex**
No Scouts tonight as it's half-term. I've been practicing my dice throwing though as it's Scout Beetle Drive tomorrow.

**Friday 22nd May**
**Skip**
A fantastic Scout meeting tonight as there was no one here, just me. I took great delight in sending Lee home when he

turned up. I texted his mother to say that he was on his way back and I told him that his mother should read her emails. The sheets of timber have been painted and we need to start nailing to make the pockets.

## Saturday 23rd May
## Alex

Tonight we went to the Beetle Drive in the Scout Hut. It was packed. There was loads of noise and running around. Skip explained the rules and off we went. I thought Scouts were noisy but the parents are far worse. There is no beer at Scout events but some of the parents had dropped the Scouts off early and then gone across the road to the pub so they were in high spirits. Sarah-Jane's dad did not appear with them back at the Scout Hut despite being in the pub as well. We had only been going for a minute when Tegan's dad (Gunner) shouted "John Lennon" and the adults laughed. I don't know why it was so funny. He's only famous for an airport so far as I'm aware. When we restarted, Tegan's daddy shouted "beetle" and Skip went over to check. He told him that he had only drawn the body. He told Skip that his beetle was a "Tetra-amelia". No one knew what he was talking about so Skip made him go and write it on the whiteboard. No one was any the wiser so Tegan's daddy got no points and was sent off to make the teas and coffees as he obviously wasn't going to play the game properly. He would get on well with Barnaby.

In the interval tell-tale Trudy came told me that Sarah-Jane was doing very well. Apparently she wasn't throwing the dice like most people, she was sort of rolling it – with her finger – so that she always got the number that she wanted. However, in a fast and furious game, no one wanted to wait half-an-hour while she had her go so nobody wanted to be in her group so after the interval Sarah-Jane got a table to herself and in a group of one with no moving up or down of tables.

At the end of the evening the Scout with the most points (excluding Barnaby) won a prize. The winner was Trudy and her prize was a bottle of whisky. Skip announced, "There must be some mistake." Trudy said that there had been no mistake. She had bought herself an adult ticket because she explained, "The kids' prizes are always naff and the food portions are really small." Unfortunately for Trudy, Akela wouldn't give Trudy the whisky and she missed out on the kids' prize as well, which was - a torch. This was won by Sarah-Jane although she hadn't been doing very well during the evening, even though she had been reinstated to full-table status after the second break. I think that Akela had fiddled the results so that Sarah-Jane won as she felt sorry for her because her dad was still in the pub. Sarah-Jane said that the torch would be very useful as it would be able to help her get home by herself. Akela said that she was hearing none of it and went over to the pub to find Sarah-Jane's dad but he wasn't there. Maybe he had forgotten that Sarah-Jane was at the Beetle Drive and had just gone straight home.

**Friday 29th May**
**Skip**
The Scouts worked hard tonight after I had finished off the painting of the bagatelle board. They had to screw the edging down and nail the pockets where they wanted them to go. They were all told to bring a hammer (I sent Marculf's dad a photo but don't know why I bothered). Most of the

143

evening was spent with a bang, bang, bang as the pockets appeared out of nowhere. After that we had to number the pockets with the scores. I gave the two Scout teams a couple of black permanent marker pens and a letter / number stencil. I showed them how to line the numbers up, mark through the stencil and continue on. We had the lower numbers at the top, and the higher numbers at the bottom, everything from 10 to 250. All we need to do now is build a frame for the boards, clamp it all together with some sash fasteners and we're done.

I have bought a couple of wood-burning pen sets. For the front of the board Scouts have burnt, "3rd Chislehurst Scout Group. The World's Largest Bagatelle Board" in huge letters into a length of wood. For the back I have marked off a small rectangle each for the Scouts to burn their individual names. They were told that they could be as inventive as they liked. Some have gone curly, some are very messy, others are really well done. It was a productive and useful session though as we could incorporate "how not to get burnt" into the activity. "And what to do if or, more relevantly, when we do get burned," I should have added.

The Scouts worked so well in their patrols tonight. Whilst some were nailing, others were practising their fire lighting skills outside. The only fly in the ointment was Jake's dad, Gavin, who was supposed to be in charge outside and leading by example, but instead was mucking about with a battery and wire wool at the end of the meeting and managed to catch the wire wool alight, having failed to do so all evening. He tried to blame it on one of the Scouts but Jake said that it was his dad.

I was so pleased with the Scouts tonight, makes it all worthwhile. Let's hope we can continue this great effort into June.

Marculf told me tonight that he didn't want a baby, he wanted a puppy, like Chloe. I'm not sure what Marculf's talking about but hopefully he does.

## Friday 29th May
### Alex
Tonight was bagatelle part two and campfire night. I did a few pockets and made sure that my nails weren't coming out of the other side of the board. I brought a really good claw hammer. Marculf brought a sledge hammer which he had to leave in the corner of the Scout Hut.

We had to burn our names into a length of wood that is going to go on the top of the bagatelle board. I burned my name and then Tegan put hers in the box above cos she said that as she is petrol leader she is more important. When she finished and was off doing something else I put a heart between our two names so now it looks like it says Tegan loves Alex. Ha,ha!

Skip told us all about how to make a good fire - again. There are two types of fire. There's the cooking one where you start with tinder which is stuff smaller than a matchstick, then kindling which is stuff smaller than a pencil, then small logs which is stuff smaller than a wrist. Each time you build a tepee shape so that you have air, fuel and, with a match, heat. If we were to move up to a camp fire then there is a fourth level which is large logs. Apparently there is no maximum size for a campfire and so anything goes. Trees, woods, even whole forests can go on. Tonight we were cooking so only levels one to three applied. But there was a big catch. No matches allowed! Gavin was our parent-helper tonight. Gavin is Jake's dad and he says that he's something in the city. Well, if he speaks like that he can't be doing anything really important. I think he means that he's someone in the city, like everyone who's in the city is someone, and there are millions of them. Skip taught us how to start a fire with potassium permanganate. You only need a teaspoonful and some anti-freeze. We also played with wire wool and a battery. When we were doing flag down Gavin tried to set fire to the Scout Hut and Skip told him off. He said that it was one of the Scouts, but I don't know which one. Next week we are going to learn how to use penknives safely. We can bring penknives if we have one. I have one. Any serious Scout should have their own penknife.

**Saturday 30th May**
**Skip**
I went to tidy up the Scout Hut this morning after last night's activities. One thing that I needed to do was move the bagatelle boards off the floor. This became impossible and I quickly deduced that some of the Scouts had been a little too keen with their nailing and had nailed the boards to the wooden floor. In the end I had to use one of the claw hammers that was inevitably left behind, and gently prised the boards from the floor. Now we are left with a number of little holes in the floor, a bit like a giant teabag. Still, no one will notice, apart from Akela. I checked on the wood burning work to make sure that nothing untoward had appeared and found that someone had doctored "Alex" so now it looks likes, "Tegan" loves "Ale XX." Very funny.

## Saturday 30th May
## Alex

Josh came round to play. Because we're Scouts we don't sit on our backsides doing diddly-squat which is what Skip says some young people do so we went into the garden to get the out in Scouting. I asked Josh what we should do and cos I told Josh at Scouts when we did drugs that mummy had loads of weeeeed in our garden, Josh said Let's do weeds. I told him that I didn't want to be skinnier but I thought it would be okay to try just a little bit, anyway we won't going to be driving anywhere today. You can't have good fires with green stuff so we had a good hunt around and we found some ivy leaves that had gone brown. We also found some holly leaves that had gone brown but Skip told us that we can't do sosages on a holly stick cos it's poisonous so we didn't use that. Anyway it was a bit prickly so that was another harmful thing that Tegan didn't mention. We thought that we would smoke it instead of just eating it. I don't think eating it would taste very nice. Anyway Tegan said that we should put it in cakes and cooking and stuff. I suppose I could put a few leaves in mummy's casserole when she's not looking but we don't have many of those this time of year and it's going to look a bit obvious if I put them in the salad so we decided to stick to smoking. Anyway, smoking can't be that harmful. We do enough of it on camp what with sitting round the camp fire and stuffing stuff in the incinerator. Skip says that if we sit with the prevailing wind (i.e. south west) behind us and the camp fire is in front of us then the camp fire smoke will blow away from us but the problem is that Skip always sits where we should so we always get the smoke. We weren't going to get much smoke with just a few ivy leaves anyway, or so I thought.

147

We went into daddy's shed cos he wasn't in cos he had gone to the pub to watch West Ham and we had a look round for some newspaper to make cigarettes but all we found were some nice shiny magazines in a drawer that were all about posh buildings in London and there were some called Mayfair and I know that's about posh buildings cos it's next door to Park Lane on Monopoly and it's worth £400 and Matthew always buys it. Maybe we should let daddy buy it. We couldn't find any newspaper but Josh said that if we went to Sainsbury's we could get a News Shopper which is free so that's what we did but we didn't buy anything but the New Shopper's huge and we could do lots of smoking with just one copy. Then we tore long strips out and rolled up the leaves. Then we couldn't make the paper stay in place so we sort of twisted and tucked it and it sort of stayed in place. Then we didn't have any matches and we never have any matches in the house but we did have a battery and Matthew showed me when I was in Cubs how to light a fire without matches which Skip had showed him it was another way. What you have to do is get a battery and a bit of silver foil to connect between the two ends with a little bit of foil in the middle with a little bit of cotton wool on the little bit in the middle which will light cos it gets hot. We got some silver foil from under the sink but we couldn't find any cotton wool so we used the fluff from our tummy buttons cos that's what Bear Grills says makes excellent tinder which is the stuff to start fires. I had a bit of fluff and Josh had loads cos I had a bath last night and Josh said he couldn't remember when he last had a bath so all his tinder was building up in his tummy button. We put it on the battery thing and, guess what diary? It lit! Now we're behind daddy's shed cos what we were doing was illegal. Then we tried to light our cigarettes from the flame but I think you have to puff or blow. Anyway the fluff lit the newspaper and then the ivy got really smoky and hot so we dropped it and it landed on all the strips of News Shopper cos we were thinking of getting ready to go into business selling weeeeed cigarettes then we had a little camp fire at the back of the shed and then a big camp fire and then mummy came running down the garden and screamed, "What are you doing?" and she didn't wait for an answer and it was horrible. So mummy ran away into the house and I said to Josh that maybe we should get a bucket of water like we do when we have a fire at Scouts. So we went and got the hose cos then we thought that a hose would be better than a bucket but it wouldn't reach cos we were down the end of the garden and it used to reach but Matthew had been chopping lots of bits off the end of the hose to make earwig traps during the holidays.

Then we didn't know what to do so we hid.

But we didn't want to burn to death cos that would be worse than death by drugs or smoking or drinking so we hid round the front and mummy would know what to do. We were very well hid cos I had made a really good survival camp under the buddleia bush that never gets cut back and two people can fit into it. Then people starting stopping in the street and getting out their phones and pointing and there was loads of crackling noises and smoke. Then we heard nar nar, nar nar and before we knew it a great big fire engine had arrived and stopped outside the house and the firemen all jumped out and there were loads of them. They were unrolling their hose and mummy came running out of the front door and she screamed at the fireman, there are two boys and one's my son and I DON'T KNOW where they are.

149

I didn't want to get told off but I didn't want mummy to think that we were burning to death so I didn't know what to do but Josh did. He called out, Mrs xxxxx, we're here, under the bush. And mummy came over and said what are you doing and I said surviving, mummy. Then she told us to come out.

I told her that I had built a survival camp so that's where we should go in an emergency a bit like in the second world war when people had to go below ground in their gardens or like the government had bunkers for when the Russians were going to attack. Mummy then told us that at this particular moment it would probably be more preferable if the Russians had attacked then she told us to wait on the lawn whilst she went and told the firemen that we were alive. I don't know why mummy thinks that it's a good idea if the Russians attack us. Maybe she thinks that they will bring her some vodka.

Then mummy came back onto the front lawn and we were just sitting there not knowing what to do cos mummy had told us not to move and there were loads more people on the other side of the pavement all staring so mummy went over to the back of the fire engine and told them all to really big big sweary off and some did but most didn't.

We had to wait on the grass for quite a long time but eventually the firemen put their big hose away and took their helmets off and they were quite hot so mummy went and got them all a drink and she brought them all a big jug of Belvoir Elderflower and Rose Cordial which she gets from Waitrose which is my favourite but it's really expensive and I knew that there wasn't a lot left this morning so by now there probably wasn't much at all but I didn't say anything to the fireman cos of what they had just done. They're very brave. I thought they may know James Ketchell cos he's brave so I asked the smiley one but he said no. He then sat down on the grass with us and he asked us if we knew what started the fire and I was going to say that I didn't know, but I did so then I thought that I'd better just say matches but that wasn't true either. I didn't want to tell the fireman that we had been lighting our tummy fluff with a battery, although most of it wasn't mine but then Josh said we've been smoking weeeeed. Then the fireman said where and we said behind the shed and then he asked us where we got our weeeed from and did we have to pay for it which was a bit strange. We told him that it was free and mummy was growing it in the garden. Then he laughed and said that in that case there wouldn't be much left and all the firemen laughed and the smiley one got up and said that they were sorry about all the expensive whiskey that's all gone but he's glad that we were okay and that they were going to go back to the fire station to fill up with water. I think the firemen meant that they had drunk the whiskey cos they were thirsty and I didn't expect daddy would mind too much.

I did tell the smiley one that he could fill up his fire engine with our hose but he told us not to worry as it would take quite a bit of time and they had to go back to the fire station to be prepared (like Scouts) for the next couple of Herberts to set fire to their dad's shed. So I said thank you but we're Alex and Josh and waved as they got into their fire engine and Josh called out thank you for saving Alex's dad's shed cos he (i.e. me) would be in so much trouble if anything happened to it and the firemen all laughed and off they went and Josh stuck his fingers up at the people on the other side of the road that were still gawping.

Mummy came out and said that we were going to face the music when daddy came home and we'd better go round the side to the back garden to inspect the damage and no we couldn't have any Belvoir Elderflower and Rose Cordial and oh dear when we got round the back. Mummy's lovely lawn was all trampled and had gone from nice green grass to mud and brown and wet, but the worst of it was that all the plants were all withered and black and then we saw that where daddy's shed was – well, now wasn't. It was just a load of black bits of wood like after a great big fab camp fire with You'll Never Get to Heaven in Akela's Bra or London's Burning, London's Burning only this wasn't a camp fire it was daddy's shed. Mummy came out the back and I said oh dear to mummy and it was probably better if I was dead cos daddy would kill me when he came home from the pub and should I phone Gary at So Shawl Services now? Mummy said no daddy won't and we don't need Gary and human life is sacred and that was a comfort so I said come on Josh let's go and watch TV cos that will be safer for today at least but when I turned to see where he was he had gone. So I had to go indoors and sit and watch TV and wait to face the music all by myself and I was very scared.

When daddy came home he was all smiley cos West Ham had won and he came and sat next to me in the sitting room and gave me a hug and then he said that I smelt all smoky and I said of course I did cos I was a Scout. Then I asked daddy if all daddies had a shed and he said that no but those that didn't would always want one cos every daddy loves his shed. So then I asked him what was the worse thing that could happen to a shed and he said blown up, blown away or burnt down. So I said oh and in what order of worstness would he put those three and he said why and then mummy came in and gave daddy a piece of paper from our insurance company file and a cheque and said it's alright dear, your shed is insured as I've checked and here's a cheque from me for the excess. Then daddy said, what's happened to my shed and mummy said that it hadn't been blown up and it hadn't blown away and daddy went all white and I said sorry daddy, I'm really sorry, especially cos all your Mayfairs and Penthouses have all got burned and the firemen drank all your expensive whisky then mummy looked at daddy and daddy looked at me and then mummy went into the kitchen and no one said anything then mummy came back into the sitting room and gave me ten pounds from the car parking jar that never usually gets touched and told me to go and find Josh and buy some ice cream each and there was no rush to come back.

So I went round to Josh's house and I knocked on his door and he said like he was trying to be his dad but it wasn't his dad cos we know where he is, don't we diary? And he said like he was a boy trying to be a man, Josh isn't in. So I said that Josh had four pounds for ice cream. Then he opened the door and said he had been down the garden and had just got in and was I still alive? Of course I was still alive and I'm still alive tonight to write my diary. I didn't say that mummy had given me ten pounds cos then he would know that I couldn't do maths. I can do maths I just wanted to keep two pounds so that Scottie Dog could have some ice cream later cos it's probably quite hot under my bed with all that bubble wrap. We went to Jimmy's [the newsagents] and for four pounds each we could buy a litre each of Kelly's Vanilla Cornish Dairy Ice Cream and Jimmy gave us a plastic spoon each. We then went into the churchyard to eat it cos it was nice and quiet, well by the time we got to the porch so we could sit down it was more like drink it. Then an old lady came down the path and into the porch and it was Mrs xxxxx who lives opposite the church and has lived there all her life and she's about two hundred years old I think and she said what are you two boys doing? And Josh said eating ice cream and she said I don't know what the world's coming to. When I was your age we used to have one scoop on a cone now you're eating enough for a family of four for a month in one sitting. It's disgraceful. Mutter, mutter, mutter. Then she disappeared inside the church to say some sorry prayers hopefully and so it was time for me to go back home.

When I got back indoors and mummy was in the sitting room and all her eyes had run black down her face like they had melted and I asked her where's daddy and she said he's gone to the pub so I asked her if he had forgotten something cos he had been there most of the afternoon and she said that the only thing that he has forgotten is that you (that is me) and Matthew are the most precious two things in the world and then I started to cry and if my eyes were the sort that melted they would have melted all down me but they're not so they didn't. Then I said to mummy what about you cos you're the most precious thing in the world to me and then she squeezed her eyes shut and she had tears leaking out and down her face and her eyes melted some more and then she gave me a squeeze so tight that I thought I was going to burst and so I thought I better say something so that she would know that I wasn't too upset so I said mummy? and she said yes. So I said mummy, what's erectile dysfunction?

Mummy s
have been
today? Mu
any childre
and then n

Mummy re
going to po
some Belvc
two pound
have to wai
bought her
Then we dr
fish and ch
mummy onl
in batter. N
daddy come
see me I just _____ ___ know that he s safe.

does she know what's going on and sl
away every tear from their eyes"
Scottie Dog is now in bed with n
away.

## Sunday 31st May
## Skip
I can't wait for Sc
going on at Alex'
there was a fi
car. I know
being a l
fire th
tak

## Saturday 30th May
## Very Late, Probably Early Morning
## Alex

My pillow's all wet and I can't sleep. I don't want to lose my daddy. Josh has lost his daddy (sort of, but he will come back eventually unless he's killed someone which I don't think he has) and he said that it's no fun not having a daddy at home to play with every day and make him toast and marmite and show him how to make paper aeroplanes and to tuck him in and give him a kiss at bedtime and adults don't understand what it's like for their children when they lose each other. Please come home daddy. For some reason Chloe has just sent me a text and it's really late and how

he says, "He will wipe
nd I hope so Chloe and
e and he's wiping my tears

uts next Friday to find out what's been
s family's house. I drove past yesterday and
e engine and this morning there was a police
that the police can sometimes been accused of
it slow reaching an emergency, but if there's been a
en you would have thought that the police would have
en less than a day to arrive. I'll have to get Hugo to have a
word with Alex to find out what's going on.

### Sunday 31st May
### Alex

When I got up this morning there was no one else around
and it was quite early but it was sunny but all the curtains
were still closed and Harriet [the cat] was scratching to go
out so I thought that mummy had gone missing as well so I
went to mummy's room (cos I didn't know if I could call it
daddy's room anymore but I'm going to be brave for
mummy) and there was loads of big snoring like a big fat pig
so I knew that daddy was at home at last thank goodness.
He might have just got lost coming home from the pub cos
he had lost his torch. I went in the bathroom and then had
my wash and did my teeth and things, the things that I'm
supposed to do on camp and never do and then on the
landing daddy appeared and he said good-morning and
sssh! cos mummy's still asleep and he went in the bathroom
and I knew that I could call it mummy's and daddy's room

156

again. I went up to the bathroom door and I said I love you daddy to the door but I don't know if he heard me cos the tap was going so I went back to my bedroom and I wrote him a note and I put on it I love you daddy and I want you to tuck me up and give me a kiss goodnight each night. Then I stuck it under the bathroom door. When I walked back past mummy and daddy's door again the door was a little bit open and there was STILL big snoring STILL like a big fat pig and I thought well it can't be mummy but it was but I won't ever tell her cos I think that she's sad enough for one week.

I went downstairs to get my breakfast and there was a RAT TAT TAT TAT TAT TAT on the door when I was washing up. Now that I'm a Scout I can get my own breakfast. I had cereal and juice and an egg and beans and sosages and jam (on its own). Daddy was in the toilet and mummy was in her sty (ha, ha) so I opened the door and said to the policeman that there was a bell so why did he make so much noise when there was a bell and daddy's in the toilet and mummy's asleep and they said that they need to speak to them and could they come in and there were two of them AND a lady cos ladies can be policemen as well. I told them that it was still really early cos the curtains were still closed and the policeman lady said it was half past eleven. So I went and told daddy that there were some noisy policemen downstairs and he came down in his dressing gown and told me to go away so as it was half past eleven it was elevenses so I went and got my elevenses but I wasn't very hungry and I was really worried cos it's the second time this year that the policemen have come to visit us but they weren't able to go into daddy's shed this time and I'm so sorry daddy but I couldn't tell him cos he was dealing with the policemen.

157

When the policemen went daddy came into the kitchen and mummy came in and said that there had just been a little misunderstanding with what happened yesterday with the ivy but how did she know and she said that Josh's mum had rung up yesterday evening and told her and no one was in any trouble. Then mummy asked me how I managed to light a fire without matches. I told her that Skip had showed Matthew and Matthew had showed me and anyway Skip showed me all sorts of ways last week and matches are the last thing that you need to light fires.

This evening we went for a pizza in Bromley. We were going to go to Pizza Express in Royal Parade but mummy said that there were too many wagging tongues around Chislehurst at the moment. I don't know why this is a problem cos mummy says that Chislehurst is full of wagging tongues. Maybe they're just all wagging all at the same time at the moment or a little bit more than usual.

We had to get a taxi cos mummy said that no one was going to be driving this evening. We hadn't been out as a family for yonks. Daddy always thinks that to put burglars off you should wave at no one in your house as you walk or drive down the street cos people who are thinking of burgling think Ah, there's someone at home. Anyway we got in the taxi and the taxi driver thinks that there's probably no one at home now and he might tell all his dodgy friends so daddy says he's just going to check on Harriet and gets out. Then mummy told the taxi driver that Harriet is our granny but she's not she's our cat. Anyway, daddy goes indoors and I said to mummy that I needed to get my penknife to practice cutting my pizza cos we were doing penknives at

Scouts soon. When I got indoors I said well done daddy for pretending that there was someone in the house and he said he hadn't but he thought he had shut Harriet in their bedroom which he had. When we got back in the taxi mummy said Was everything okay and daddy said Yes. Then he said that he had shut Harriet in their bedroom by mistake and he found her on top of the wardrobe when he opened the door and then she jumped down and ran through his legs, down the stairs and then hid behind the piano and wouldn't come out so daddy's left her there. I suppose now the taxi driver doesn't think we have a cat, more likely Super Gran.

We had a really yummy pizza each and I was allowed to have a starter and a pudding. I used my Midnite Manager to cut my pizza although it took quite a long time to cut it up as mummy wouldn't let me use the knife bit and the scissors were quite slow. I wanted daddy to order beer so that I could take the bottle top off with my Midnite Manager bottle opener but daddy didn't drink any beer, only water and Matthew and me we had lemonade and mummy drank a whole bottle of Champagne all by herself or so she thought. Mummy sat opposite Matthew and Matthew said Shall I top you up mummy, which is what daddy says only he doesn't say mummy he says Janette. Then he tops mummy up and the Champagne is really fizzy and it fizzes up all over the glass like a volcano only bubbles so no one's going to be killed. Then mummy goes to get a cloth and daddy's in the toilet – agaaaain! So Matthew poured some Champagne in his lemonade glass and then put some in mine but his lemonade glass was empty and mine wasn't but I still got quite a bit and it looks just like lemonade which is probably why when we did Cub camp Akela was drinking lemonade

159

all evening and had to keep going to her tent to get it and then in the morning had to go to first aid to get some Paracetamol. Matthew spilt mummy's glass twice so he had two glassfuls and I had two half fuls and daddy didn't have pudding but he did have three double espressos. Then we got the taxi home and everyone's in bed apart from ME! And I'm so glad that daddy's at home.

## Monday 1st June
### Alex

A pinch and a punch day but no pinching and punching in the Alex household, that's for sure. Matthew and me we both had headaches at breakfast and mummy said, Oh, a bit of a head which is what she said to daddy yesterday after the policemen left. Then she said that she didn't have a bit of a head and she couldn't understand why. When I came back from school I saw that the buddleia had been cut right down exposing my survival camp. Not much of a survival camp at the moment now, mind you nowhere else is in the garden at the moment. More like a survived camp. Or a not-survived camp even more like. I haven't said anything to mummy though. Hugo rang and asked me if I was okay cos there were rumours going round the village. I said that not much had happened over half-term, just a visit from the fire brigade and the police again just cos of a bit of weeeeed that went wrong. Then mummy wanted to speak to Hugo and she told Hugo that she wanted to speak to Skip and then she said to Skip You're out of control and not fit to be a Scout leader and then she said a long sweary word and put the phone down.

## Monday 1st June
### Skip

Hugo rang Alex this evening. Hugo said that Alex told him that the reason for the police visit was that Alex and been smoking dodgy cannabis. ****** ****! He's not even a teenager! In any event I would have thought that the first emergency service to call over some bad drugs would have been the one that wasn't present! That is to say the ambulance service!

And how big was this joint if they had to call the fire brigade?

Then Hugo said that Alex's mum wanted to speak to me. This was going to be interesting. I just said, "Hi Janette" and she said or rather shouted, "You are out of control and not fit to be a Scout leader!" All I could say was "pots and kettles Janette, pots and kettles," to which she said, "********!" and put the 'phone down. Charming!

## Tuesday 2nd June
## Alex
Chloe came round unannounced after tea and asked me if I wanted to go to the chill out club at [a local] church with her like straightaway so I said yes cos I like Chloe and I needed to chill as I had nearly died last week. As we walked to the church she said it's great and she went last week in half-term but didn't know many people. She said that it was chill out cos a lot of the older children were doing exams or pretend exams and were getting really stressed so it was a chance to go and calm down. In that case it would have been a good idea to bring mummy and daddy but they're probably too old for chill out club. They're also probably too young for church and will have to wait until they're the same age as Mrs xxxxx when they can start moaning about ice

161

cream. Then she said that she thought that I needed to chill after what had been going on at my house so I asked how she knew and she said she didn't know but her mum thought it would be a nice idea.

I had a great time and we did air-hockey and indoor basketball and they had a football machine and squash so there wasn't much chill out, more warm up. Then James who is a youth worker talked to us and told us that the tongue is one of the smallest parts of the body but it can do the greatest damage (like the wagging tongues of Chislehurst but James didn't say that). He then asked if we had any questions and Chloe had loads but when he asked me I said Do you know James who's climbed up oceans and swum mountains and stuff? And he laughed and said No but I bet he does cos he's got his name. Then James said that like our tongues a huge forest can be set on fire by just a small spark and so I started to cry and said that I didn't mean to burn all daddy's Mayfairs and James said that I wasn't to worry as I was in a safe place and then mummy came and picked me and Chloe up and she took Chloe home. It was good fun, it wasn't like church at all with people who look cross and tell you off for eating ice cream and stuff but I told James that I couldn't do Friday Club cos I had Scouts and he said that that was okay and I could come along when I was an Explorer and I told him I was an Explorer already just not a proper one like on Mondays.

**Tuesday 2nd June**
**Skip**
Alex's mum rang me this evening. Before I even had a chance to say, "Hallo," she said, "And another thing. I suppose you've forgotten New Year's Eve and why you were

banished to the polytunnel for two nights." "Err, it wasn't the polytunnel, it was the greenhouse." "Whatever it was it was the dog house. So don't you start spreading rumours about my husband. I've got more on you, mate!* I was flabbergasted. "Don't you remember what you said? Don't you remember what you did?" she continued. The problem is, no I don't remember. Then she said, "He's not the only one to get in a bit of a mess now and again. You and your..." It was time to bring an end to the proceedings. "Janette. I don't know what I've done, let alone your husband. Let's just call it a day shall we?" Too late, she had gone.

**Friday 5th June**
**Alex**
Tonight Skip taught us safety with penknives. I've been quite safe with my Midnite Manager because I've been using it properly, but some of the other Scouts aren't so clever. Skip showed us how to open a penknife. We have to put our fingernail in the little slot. Every blade has a slot. When we close it we use the palm of our hand against the back of the penknife blade and push. We mustn't poke with them and when we're whittling we must sit down. Skip handed out the penknives to those that didn't bring one. I brought mine. So did Jake. His isn't as good as mine, and it's older but it's luminous and it's got a corkscrew. That's not going to be much use to him until he's a man. Marculf came in waving a machete and Skip thought that we were under attack so he put Marculf in an arm-lock and then confiscated it.

As soon as it was time to open the penknives we had two casualties. The twins both got their penknives half open then grasped them like they were holding a knife ready to stab someone. They both got cuts across their fingers and

163

Jack started to cry. Then Peter cried. Then they had to go home. We then had to whittle a whistle. First we went for a walk and found a piece of elder each. Elder is good because it has a soft bit in the middle that can be poked out. Then we had to make a hole in the side of the elder and then push a stick into the middle hole after we had whittled a little gap along the stick. Then it was time to blow! Some of the Scouts (including me) managed to make a noise. Mostly the noise was not a whistle noise, more like a cat being killed. Nico couldn't make a whistle or a cat being killed noise. He said the whole evening was a waste of time when we could have all just popped down to Sports Direct and bought a whistle. He really is a stupid boy even if he is a petrol leader. When we're in the middle of the jungle and we need to attract someone's attention from across a shark-infested river we can't just pop down to Sports Direct can we? No. That's why in the jungle I will be a survivor and Nico will be eaten. All because he couldn't make a whistle. Barnaby made his whistle whistle but he also whittled the top of his finger and had to have a plaster too. Then when we put the knives away, Laura cut herself. So that was a total of four injuries for the evening which I think is a record. And that was before the fire brigade turned up. Jake had made Skip a cup of tea during the break cos his petrol was dutiful petrol this evening. Then suddenly Laura came running in and said that the hedge was on fire. We all rushed out to have a look and the whole hedge really was burning. And it was a holy hedge. Holy burns really well which is something the Scouts won't forget now. I think that Jake had something to do with it, but I'm not sure what. Skip and Crusher got the hose out and by the time the fire brigade arrived Skip and Crusher had put the fire out and one of the firemen said, "Hallo Alex" and so I said, "Hi." Then they said Have you been smoking weeeeed again? And I said No so Josh said It was Jake. And so the fireman said Oh, do you smoke weeeeed as well and Jake went all red so I bet he does cos Jake does everything. There wasn't much of the hedge left. At flag down we got told off for not using our knives properly and if we couldn't use them properly we wouldn't be able to use them at all. The, Jake put up his hand and said Please Skip, You can't tell us not to use knives cos Bear Grills says we can. Oh does he said Skip, so he told you that personally did he. Yes Skip. When I did I'm a Scout he said that Scouts are the only people in the world that are allowed and encouraged to get their knives and get muddy and not be told off for it. Yeah, said Skip, but that was probably in a different context. You would have been making mud not trying to burn down a Scout Hut. When Marculf's dad picked Marculf up at the end of the meeting, Skip gave him the machete which he had wrapped in tea-towels and said to him that we were whittling whistles not hollowing out canoes. Marculf's dad doesn't speak any English so he just smiled and nodded. Apparently any type of knife in Georgian is a knife. This must make it difficult if you want to go cutting your way through undergrowth in a jungle. Don't have Marculf with you is all I can say. Cos it would take rather a long time with him just swishing a penknife around, even with a corkscrew on it.

## Friday 5th June
## Skip
What is it about penknives that means that I have to not only have the first-aid kit on stand-by, but open and ready for action? I taught them safety with (little) knives tonight but still had several casualties. They were all happily whittling their sticks of elder to make whistles when Jake

suddenly appeared with a cup of tea. I should have known something was up. Why didn't he just tell me that the holly hedge was ablaze? Crusher rang the fire brigade but it didn't take long for us to rig up the hose from the outside tap and bring the fire under control, yet not before the hedge had gone from green to black. Then it was time for an inquisition. It appears that Jake had brought some potassium permanganate to the meeting having told his father that we were going to be doing some water purification. He then had to get hold of some sugar and what better way to get hold of some than to offer to me and Crusher a cup of tea? A small quantity of potassium permanganate mixed with sugar and then with a bit of friction applied to it will make a good flame for tinder. I had taught them one of the potassium permanganate tricks using anti-freeze, but not sugar. And how was I to know that Jake was going to mix a whole pot of potassium permanganate with a load of sugar on a tree stump by the hedge when he was supposed to be whittling, and then use his penknife blade to produce a bit of friction?! This Scouting lark appears to be getting a bit out of control.

After the fire brigade had left I thought it would be a good idea to dismiss the Scouts at the gate and not inside the hut, so the parents wouldn't be able to see what we had been up to, but I was distracted by the fact that Jake had got his penknife stuck in a piece of wood and all the parents came wandering in with that, "I'm sure that hedge was okay two hours ago" look on their faces. Jake had managed to corkscrew his penknife into a piece of wood and got it stuck. I did try to explain to him that the corkscrew was to be used for exactly that, i.e. the unscrewing of a cork, but he said that he wouldn't be able to use it until he was eighteen when he would be able to legally open a bottle of wine. I didn't bother telling him that the illegality is not in the opening of a bottle of wine but in the purchasing if you're underage but I was distracted by the fact that he was running up to meet his mother who was staring at the hedge and I needed to make sure that she was aware of where the responsibility lay. Actually, come to think of it, I think that the responsibility probably lay where I don't think I want it to...

**Friday 12th June**
**Alex**
Marculf brought his machete to Scouts again tonight and Skip confiscated it again. Marculf said to Skip that his dad had said that we were going to be whittling canoes tonight, but we weren't. Tonight was better than that. We went into the woods and built a fabulous survival shelter. Jake told Skip that he had brought along his Bear Grills' survival kit which He had been given at I'm a Scout when Bear Grills visited but Skip just said Oh cos I think he's had enough of listening to Jake talk about Bear Grills cos Bear Grills has never done anything for Skip apart from run over his phone. We had to gather long sticks and interlock them down a backbone, then cover with more sticks, moss, mud and leaves. Hugo refused to take part as he said that we are not allowed to take stuff out of National Trust woods. Skip said that we're not taking it out, we're just rearranging it. He still wouldn't take part though even though Skip's his dad. Aaron found some really good mud which was surprising because it hasn't rained for a while but he kept disappearing and coming back with big handfuls. He dropped each handful on the frame and then the rest of us spread it all over whilst Aaron went to get some more. Finally Skip asked him where he had found such a great supply and Aaron said, "I scraped

up some bare earth and peed on it." Then Skip told him off and the others started screaming and wiping their hands on each other's backs. Skip said, "Whatever possessed you to start weeing on the earth?" Aaron said that it made good mud and so Skip said, "I'm sure it does, but I've never heard of anything so revolting." So Aaron told Skip that we were in a survival situation, weren't we? And so we needed to waterproof our shelter in case it poured with rain. Then Skip asked Aaron where he had got such a revolting idea from. Aaron said, "From Bear Grills. He told me that to make the mud wet all you have to do is pee on it." Skip then just said, "Oh," and nothing else cos he knew that Aaron had met Bear Grills as well at "I'm a Scout, Get me out of here!" and Aaron knew what we are allowed to do (loads) and what we're not (not much) and he had, in fact won, and Bear Grills had given Aaron some tips. I'm not sure that Skip will ask Aaron ever again what else Bear Grills said in case it involves sick or poo or wee or knives or mud or all five. When we had finished (and it took all evening) it started to rain but no rain came into our shelter. Skip took off his shirt and scarf (that's the Scout name for a necker) and hung them by the entrance. He also took off his hiking boots and put them on the ground by the entrance. Then he crawled inside so only his feet were showing and got Tegan to take a picture of him. Maybe he thought he may have to sleep in it one night if he puts himself about a bit again like he did last new year so was trying it for size.

When we were walking back Jake told me that it was he who had burnt the hedge down last week at the Scout Hut. He said that he had made Skip a cup of tea so that he could get hold of some sugar. He then mixed it with some potassium permanganate that he had acquired (that means he stole some while he was putting it away for Skip) and was chopping it up on a tree stump during break with his penknife when it burst into flames and set the hedge on fire. When I asked him how many teaspoonfuls he had used he told me that he had used the whole pot. Thank goodness Jake isn't my petrol leader as I may well have been killed by now.

Skip brought a bottle of wine to Scouts tonight so that Jake could practice his cork screw skills. But he wasn't very good and he broke the cork off half way. Then Skip told us that you can normally push a cork into a bottle with your finger. You have to be careful cos you're increasing the pressure when you push and when you get the cork into the wine the wine then wants to spurt out cos you're still pushing very hard unless you're very careful. Jake wasn't very careful and he couldn't push with his finger so Skip got him a spoon with a narrow handle. He then had to use the handle to push down and when he did so he pushed so hard that when the cork went into the bottle the wine came rushing out. Josh said it was like his headless chicken but you can drink wine but you can't drink chicken blood. Jake made a bit of a mess of his shirt and there was wine all over the floor. I don't think that Skip was very pleased but at least he caught some of the drips in a glass that he'd brought which Jake then drunk when Skip wasn't looking. Jake asked Skip whether he was going to drink the wine now with floaty bits of cork in it and Skip said Yes once he had got home, he was just going to have to put it through a sieve and then bring it up to room temperature as it had been sitting out in the garage.

**Friday 12th June**
**Skip**

The Scouts enjoyed making their survival shelters this evening and we finished with a bit of cork screwing though I reckon it should be called "cork unscrewing." I brought along a bottle of wine for Jake to practice on. Unfortunately it was a rather good bottle of claret that I had been given for my birthday as there was not much else in the house apart from last year's sloe gin. But that's in a plastic milk bottle so that's no good. Actually I'm running a bit low so I must remember to pick some more sloes in the autumn. Maybe I can get the Scouts to help. Jake's corkscrew skills weren't really up to scratch which I suppose is hardly surprising seeing as he's never used a corkscrew before. Unsurprisingly he managed to twist and turn and pull so much that the cork broke and so he had to push it into the bottle to finish the job off and he made quite a mess. When I arrived home I had just settled down with the TV and a glass of claret with still a few bits of cork in it when I got a text from Jake's mum which said simply, "Why are you giving my son red wine to drink at Scouts?" I replied, "Hi Hannah. I wasn't, I was just letting him practice his cork-screwing skills with his penknife that he hadn't used before. Presumably you bought him the penknife so you would have known that it had a corkscrew." Then she texted back with, "Yes, but he can learn to use it when we're ready, not when you are." "I'm sorry, I just thought that it would be useful skill," I sent back. Then I added, "If it's any consolation, he's not very good at it." To which I received the reply, "Well he is now, Mr Skip, 'cos he's just uncorkscrewed two cases of Gavin's Gevrey-Chambertin Premier Cru and it's all sitting round the fireplace in the lounge whilst, 'I bring it up to room temperature, mummy.' Goodness knows what Gavin's going to say when he gets in." "Cheers?" I suggested. No reply.

## Friday 19th June
## Alex

The summer holidays are only one month away and that means one thing, summer camp! This is just like all the other camps only longer. This one is going to be proper fun. Skip says we're going away for a week. We're going to go to France Italy on an adventure camp with some other Scouts in the district.

## Friday 19th June
## Skip

I've told the Scouts that we can go to Italy and France in August as there are quite a few places available, for one reason or other, on a trip that has been planned by some of the other groups in the district, and is now being offered to us. There has been quite a bit of interest with several parents contacting me this evening.

## Saturday 20th June
## Skip

A very busy day with parents calling round to pay for little Johnny's trip to Italy and France. It seems that the price hasn't put anyone off and they're looking forward to getting rid of their kid(s) for a week or so during the holidays.

## Friday 26th June
## Alex

Tomorrow is Rotary Summer Fair on the Common. I'll be there. Skip told us to arrive at nine o'clock. We've finished the bagatelle board and we think it's the biggest in the world! Skip's asked the Guinness Book of Records people to come and have a look! We've got two sheets of wood all banged and screwed and drilled and we've all put our names on it and it's fab. We use golf balls for balls and a broom handle for hitting the balls (better use than sweeping according to Barnaby). We've all had a go this evening and I scored 630 cos I got a ball in the 250 pocket.

**Friday 26th June**
**Skip**
Tonight we had a practice on the world's largest bagatelle board. It's all ready now for it to be transported down to the Common for the Rotary Summer Fair in the morning. Hopefully the Guinness World Records people will turn up. That will put us on the map!

**Saturday 27th June**
**Alex**
Today was the fabulous Rotary Summer Fair. Rotary is an adult organisation and they like fireworks so they have a big firework event to celebrate blowing up Guy Forks in November. Rotary has a logo that Skip says is a wagon wheel. This is a bit strange. Why would a group of adults want a biscuit for a logo? There was a big logo at the Fair and Joe said it looks like a lifebelt with measles. Matthew and I got there early cos nothing much goes on in our house on Saturday morning cos mummy and daddy are in bed. So we made our own breakfast cos Matthew found some Euros and went to xxxxx [a supermarket] at the petrol station cos they take Euros there cos Marculf is from Europe and so is allowed to spend them cos foreign people are allowed to and he told us. And we had CocoPops and the expensive orange juice and eggs and bacon and sosage and bread and cheese and posh chocolates.

We helped Skip put up the mess tent frame and not the

172

canvas cos no one would be able to see what we were doing with our biggest bagatelle board in the world if it was inside. There was so much to do. We had to put pegs in the ground to stop the frame moving and then we put a tarpaulin over the frame in case it rained but it wasn't on the forecast so that's why we put the tarp up cos if it says no rain then usually it does rain. Then we put the tables up and then put the bagatelle board on top. It's two boards so we had to fix them together and then put some wood under the board so it was on a slope.

We got to the Common at eight o'clock just as Skip was arriving and he looked surprised and he asked us if we had had any breakfast and we said yes, and we've brought some Euros to buy some lunch and Skip sort of looked at us but didn't say anything.

It was one pound a go for ten golf balls and the highest score at the end of the day won a remote controlled helicopter or a bottle of whisky for the adults. There was a man who came to play and he said to me that it was very expensive cos it's one pound for ten balls and I said, No it's not when you think l how much time has gone into making it and he said Not much time by what he could see which was a bit rude. Anyway he said that he would have a go and paid one pound for ten balls and each time he played he scored 250 which was very unlikely but he did although I didn't see cos each time he shot a ball up the board he would put his arm on my shoulder and turn me round and say Who's that person or Have you been on that stall or even he said It was bad luck to look at the balls when they're being played. Anyway he scored ten times 250 which is 2500 even though one ball was resting on another which was in the 250 so he said that

that counted as two lots of 250. Then Lee came back from his break and he looked at the man and then the man wrote 2,500 on the whiteboard then his phone number, then SPENCER and we knew who he was and Lee went red though he had done nothing wrong.

Matthew and me had what mummy calls a good lunch. First we had a burger and chips and xxxxx [drink]. We had elevenses before that which was a chocolate cookie (large) from the xxxxx stall. Then we had an ice cream and Matthew then went and bought some whelks and then he was sick and had to go home and I had a shandy. Skip didn't know Matthew had been sick cos Matthew was on the teacup ride at the time so was just sick in the teacup so as not to make any mess and no one saw so he just left it there to avoid any fuss.

Then we had our picture taken for the newspaper and for the Visit Chislehurst website cos we need a Visit Chislehurst website so that people know that we have caves and shops and no one had scored more than 2,500 so Spencer was going to get the whisky for the adult competition and Josh had scored 990 for the children so he was going to get the helicopter. Then I wanted one more go but I only had fifty pence so Josh said I could have five goes but I said I couldn't beat Spencer but Josh said I could if we did retrospective scoring. I really didn't know what he was talking about but he said You watch so I had four goes and each go I scored NOUGHT. Then on the fifth go I hit the golf ball not so hard and it went up board one and then board two and then stopped and rolled down into the ten. Then Josh said Be Prepared and got out the letter / number stencil that is Skip's AND a big black marker pen and put the stencil over the 10 and didn't want to move the stencil cos the numbers would be wobbly so he filled in 789 so now the 10 score was now 10789 and Josh said Winner! Then Spencer came back and we said I've won and he said cheat and he put took the pen and wrote SPENCER WINNER on the board and he didn't want the whisky and so Josh had the whisky and awarded it to himself cos I couldn't take the whisky home cos mummy had said that she never wants to hear or see whisky in our house again. Then Spencer said Gimmee the 'copter so we had to and he said I gonna av a go nar. And he got it out of the box and got the remote out and put the batteries in and charged up the helicopter then said Watch this and the helicopter went up when he pushed the stick on the remote control, then he said Time for a turn and he moved the stick to the left and then to the right and then he shook the box then he wobbled the stick round and round and the helicopter just keep going and going and going, and it went over the Common, over the trees and disappeared and Spencer put the remote down and said Sweary! Sweary! Sweary! and he should have read the box cos the box said For indoor use only and he walked off. Josh got the pen and crossed off WINNER and put BIG LOSER and we all laughed and I said I would take the remote home to make a rocket launcher or something. Then Chloe turned up and said she was sorry but she hadn't felt too good earlier on so we told her about SPENCER LOSER and she smiled and took the marker pen and wrote on the board The first shall be last and gave me a nice smile and her hair looks different.

I helped Skip pack up and he was waiting for the van to come and he said that I could go home cos we had finished and I had been very, very helpful (Skip used two "verys". No one else has had two verys from Skip.) I told him that it was okay and that I would go home when we had loaded up the van so I waited with him and Hugo but I didn't tell him why I didn't want to go home which was because we always have to tidy the house on Saturday afternoons but by evening it's too late and Matthew would have to do it by himself or it doesn't get done until next Saturday when there's no more mess, not twice as much anyway so I don't know why it has to be done EVERY week.

Anyway, I walked home and when I walked up the drive I saw on the lawn oh I could not believe it it was the helicopter and it had landed (crash landed probably) and I went indoors and said Mummy a helicopter has crash landed on our lawn and she screamed and said What have you been doing now? And I said nothing and told her that I had picked it up then I showed her and she smiled. I had the box and the remote control so I took it into my room and charged it up and it works perfectly so I sent Chloe a text and I said The last shall me first, i.e. me and she sent me back a smiley face and J.L.Y and I have no idea what's she's talking about.

Mummy said that Matthew was in bed and would I mind putting the Hoover around and I said around what and mummy was a little bit sweary and said the carpet but then smiled when I told her I was a Guinness World Record holder even though the man hadn't turned up, anyway I'm not cos it's the Scouts but I am part of the world record. Then mummy asked if I had seen a hundred Euros cos daddy put them somewhere cos he's going to France on Monday and I thought, "Whoops" but said No mummy cos that wasn't a lie cos I hadn't seen them all together just a few at a time. Then she said that my breath smelt of beer so I told her that I had had one but I made sure that I told her that it was only a small one cos she looked quite cross. I should have said that it was one with no alcohol in it but I think she understood.

## Saturday 27th June
### Skip

Rotary Summer Fair Day. Despite having asked for Scouts and parents to sign up on the rota to help man the bagatelle game no one at all had signed up. However by lunchtime I had fifteen Scouts and five parents wanting to know, "If you need any help?" Yes, I do, please. I would like you to SIGN THE B****Y ROTA SO THAT I CAN P – L – A – N!!!" "Er, what rota?" came the, it has to be said, rather pathetic reply.

Alex and Matthew turned up at the crack of dawn although they said that they had already had breakfast. That was very organised of their mother, bearing in mind that she once told me that the only things that she sees on Saturday mornings are from her back. I never have quite worked out what she was talking about but one thing's for sure, it would be mighty difficult to make a cup of coffee or cook breakfast from that position.

Alex stayed all day and beyond the call of duty. He didn't want to go home although Matthew had to because he didn't feel well. I'm not sure what's going on at home for Alex not to want to go home. I assume his mother would have been up by mid-afternoon. I did try to get him to tell me but he wouldn't and I didn't want to push it. I'll just keep an eye on him. In the meantime, I'm going to give him a "Well Done" certificate to show that all his hard work is appreciated.

## Sunday 28th June
## Skip
Sunday morning lie-in was interrupted by a call from Alex's mother (from her bed it sounded like) demanding to know why I had given him beer! When I asked her, "When?" she replied that it didn't matter when, I wasn't to do it. I patiently explained that I hadn't, whenever it was, but I was just interested to know when I was supposed to have given Alex beer. "You're not supposed to give it to him at all!" she shouted at me down the 'phone. I tried another tack. "When did Alex say that I had given him beer?" I asked her kindly. "He didn't but he smelt of it." "When did he smell of it?" "Yesterday." "At the Fair?" "Presumably, unless he popped into The Imperial Arms on the way home." "Well, I can assure you that I didn't give your son any beer or anything else alcoholic to drink." "Just make sure you don't. There's too much drinking going on in this country. Even Josh is on the whisky now." Then the 'phone went dead. Strange woman.

## Skip
## Friday 3rd July
At flag-down I presented Alex with his "Well done" certificate and he beamed. I explained to the Scouts that the reason Alex was awarded the certificate was because he stayed beyond the call of duty at the Rotary Fair. "Only cos he didn't want to do the housework at home!" said Barnaby with a smirk on his face. So that was the reason. Nevertheless, I've never been one for motives, the fact is he was of more use than any of the parents, none of whom have ever been awarded a "Well done" certificate. I should have some "Poorly done!" certificates made up though. I could get rid of loads of those. "For helping at Rotary Fair – Poorly

done!" "For picking your child up from Scouts twenty minutes late because you were in the pub – Poorly done!" What about, "For ringing me up on a Sunday morning because it can't wait until Monday? – Poorly done!" "For paying the Spring Term's subs in September – Poorly done!" Goodness knows what I'd get back in return if I tried that on. I think this idea will just have to stay within the pages of my private diary.

### Friday 10th July
### Alex
One week and then it's holiday time. Barnaby asked Nico where he was going for his holidays and Nico said that he was going to Tenerife. Barnaby looked at him and said, "I can't believe that you're going to Tenerife, it's full of chavs." Nico just smiled. Nico lives in the biggest house in Chislehurst. If Nico's parents didn't want to meet any chavs I'm sure that they could have gone somewhere else.

### Friday 17th July
### Alex
No Scouts today as it's the start of the summer holidays and Skip says he has to get ready for France Italy. It's not really the start of the holidays proper as we only broke up at lunchtime. But already half of Chislehurst has disappeared off to the med, that's what mummy says, wherever that is. Some of us went to the Scout Hut with our daddies for a tidy up. I know the name of at least one Scout who's gone away already. Barnaby told me that he had got a text on his new phone today from Nico, which said, "Do you want to come and play?" Barnaby texted back and said that he would and where was Nico. Nico texted back and said that he was at home. Barnaby put on his shoes and walked all the way up

the hill to Nico's looks like a castle house. When he got there he knocked on the front door but there was no answer so he knocked again. Then he texted Nico and said. "I'm outside your house, but no one's answering. Where are you?" A few minutes later he got a text from Nico that said, "Ha, ha – my Tenerife home".

## Friday 24th July
### Alex
France Italy is two weeks and one day away. Skip won't have to do anything on this camp as the camp is done by a separate company, called ABC Adventure Travel, slogan, "Adventure Beyond Compare!" We have to have a practice camp next week so that we know what we're doing. We also have to meet the other Scouts that we're going to be sleeping with. This is a good idea as we need to know who's likely to be sick. We're going to Thriftywood Camp in Essex. Skip is coming. He said that Essex is a bit cheap but we shouldn't worry about it.

## Friday 31st July
### Alex
Camp started at seven o'clock this evening which didn't give mummy much time to give me dinner so she said that we could have fish and chips in Brentwood on the way to the campsite. We found a place called Fred the Fish and mummy parked outside and took me in for two cod and chips. It wasn't that cheap so I told the lady behind the counter. She said, "Yer whaaat?" so I said again, "That's not very cheap. Skip said Essex is cheap," and she then said that my Skip was well right but I could only have a discount if I was an ohayepee and it was a Wednesday, which it isn't so I don't know why she even told me that.

When we arrived at Thriftywood I found out that we were staying in the tented village which is like something like red Indians have only we don't have to get out our mallets. I've stayed at one before when I was sick through the sluts. I'm in a tented tent with a boy called Logan and another boy called Eli and a girl called Samantha. Samantha is sweet. I had never slept with a girl before. I said that she could have the top bunk cos she started to cry when I asked her what colour her pyjamas were then she went out. I said that I would go in the other top bunk cos if I was sick it won't smell so bad. I didn't tell the others that. There are lots of leaders who are coming to France Italy and some are on this tented camp. There is a nice man who Skip calls Touchy who is a Cub leader but he is coming to France Italy. He has made a clock with eleedee lights which he has put up in the messy tent. He says it can tell the temperature outside the messy tent and inside the messy tent. It can tell the date, how many days in seconds to go until France Italy and how high the tented village is above sea level, all in bright green eleedee. What I'm not sure that it can do is tell the time.

We were given some time to unpack our rucksacks. Samantha came back in and said that Clair said that on her sheet her name is Sam. Uh, oh! I packed my rucksack myself so I know where everything goes. We have to practice packing our rucksacks at Scouts so that we know what is important and what isn't. The heavy things go at the top and the light things at the bottom. Then you have to put the things that you will need near the sides of the rucksack, things like sweets and drinks and stuff. The things that we won't need, like soap and toothbrush and underpants, they go inside somewhere. It's funny that we have to pack our rucksacks so neatly cos when we unpack we just pull all the stuff out and leave it on the floor. After we had unpacked, that means, covered the sluts with our stuff we had to go to the messy tent to report in for a game. We had to play a wise game. Wise games are ones that are played outside, normally with loads of Scouts. It's called a wise game because it's only for clever people, so I don't know why Aaron was involved. The one that we played was called "Autographs". The leaders and Explorers had to go to different parts of the camp site and we had to find them, get an autograph and come back and have the autograph signed off by Touchy in the messy tent each time before getting another one. Each time we got an autograph the leader or Explorer also gave us a mark out of ten depending on how easy or hard it was to find the leader or Explorer. The harder the leader or Explorer was to find, the higher the score. No one found Aaron. Aaron is still a Scout but he was allowed to be an Explorer for the evening cos he said that he had found a great place to hide.

When we had finished our wise game we had supper in the messy tent. There were five boys at a table in the corner of the tent. I don't know their names. They were told off cos they didn't play Skip's wise game and had gone into a tent to play cards. They said that they couldn't be bothered to play a stupid wise game. They probably wouldn't have been allowed to even if they had wanted though. Clair said that they were too cool for school and they all smiled although they weren't too cool for school they were only about eleven years old so would have to go to school. Too thick for school maybe. Clair is the nice lady who is organising France Italy. She's a Skip as well but I don't know where. No one calls her Skip. Maybe they don't have lady Skips. I will call her Clair as well although it's probably not her real name. I don't think she's as old as Skip. She actually looks quite young.

When we went to bed (without Samantha, she had disappeared as well) Eli got out a Mega Family Fun pack of Haribos. There were eighty packs inside which was enough to feed the whole campsite. We ate the lot. About an hour later Eli was sick. Fortunately he missed his clothes. I thought I should go and get Clair who is the nice lady in charge but Eli said that if his mummy found out that he had been sick then he wouldn't be allowed to go to France Italy so he got out of bed and went and got a dustpan and brush from the messy tent. He told Clair that he just wanted to sweep our floor cos it was a bit messy. He then brushed up the sick (the bits that hadn't fallen through the sluts) and the Haribo wrappers. He then went outside to get rid of it. He found an empty tent all zipped up so he quietly unzipped it and brushed the sick and the Haribo wrappers onto the floor. He then went and washed the dustpan and brush under the tap by the path and then swept up some dust and then went back to the messy tent, showed Clair and swept it in the bin. Then he felt sick again but he wasn't, fortunately. He said that Aaron was in the messy tent wrapped in a towel but didn't like to ask. Maybe it was the foreign food we had been eating for supper. Clair said that we could eat some food from France Italy to get our plates ready so for supper we had Chicken Calmer. I asked Clair whether it was French or Italian food and she said Indian which is where she said we would end up in our kayaks if we don't stop when we are told to when we are in France Italy. Now we are finally in bed with no more dramas although we've now found that there are slugs climbing up the tent walls so Eli has started to stab them all with his penknife although Skip had told us

183

no stabbing with our penknives. Skip has said that in the morning we will be doing team-building and raft-building and that we should be careful on the lake as it contains terrorpins and piranhas.

## Saturday 1st August
### Alex
I did pinch and a punch on Eli this morning then he hit me so I don't think I'll be doing that again to him. This morning it was 22.8 degrees of heat (thanks to Touchy otherwise I would just call it hot). It was only 20.6 degrees outside. This is because there is a lot of heat in the messy tent what with all the cooking going on. We did problem solving this morning. We had a big bit of scrambling net with different size holes that was hanging between two trees and we had to get all the Scouts through without touching the sides. Once a hole had been used, it couldn't be used again. We were going quite well with barrel rolls, commando rolls and a Frisbee flop (non-airborne). We lifted up Laura and told her to pretend she was dead. That is to say long and stiff, although she was still allowed to breathe. We then passed her through one of the higher up holes. I was the first to go so I chose the easiest hole (still got told off). Nathan was last to go which was a mistake because he's so fat and wouldn't fit through any of the holes so I got out my penknife and cut out one length to make a bigger hole out of two smaller ones. Then an instructor had a paddy and said that I had ruined their netting so I told them that they didn't say that we couldn't cut it and they said that they said that we mustn't touch it and I said that I didn't, my penknife touched it and then they said that Eli had been through the same hole and I said that he had only gone through half of it and in any case now that I've cut out a bit it's now a new hole and I had to go and

184

tell Skip what I had done but I didn't I just went for a wee. Talk about argumentative. Who do they think they are? They're only instructors. When I came back I told the instructors that Skip had said that he would sort it out and they just said that was fine. I don't see why I should get told off for using my initiative.

Aaron was unable to be found last night because he had found a wooden pallet and floated into the middle of the lake like a raft. He was supposed to make it difficult for us to get his autograph, not impossible. At breakfast he said that he was an A-list celebrity and that's the sort of thing that A-list celebrities do to avoid having to be pestered by their fans. When Laura asked him which celebrity he thought he was he said that he was Michael Jackson which is a bit stupid cos Aaron is not American, nor is he black or brown or pure white and he's not dead either. Although he would have been if he had fallen in the lake and the terrorpins and piranhas had got him.

Then we all did team-building on a large log. We all had to stand on it and then swap places so that we ended up in age order. We weren't allowed to talk which made it harder as we had to work out months as well as years. In the end we managed it and I was the tenth youngest. The instructors said KISS which I think means Keep It Simple Scouts, which we didn't. Skip said it was more like SHIFT but I didn't hear what that stood for. Then we had to rearrange into house number order. This was a real challenge what with the log only being fifteen centimetres wide. We weren't allowed to talk again. It took forever. We weren't allowed to fall off otherwise we would have to have gone back to the start. Laura made the whole thing really difficult cos she doesn't have a house number cos she lives in a posh house in a posh road so she was trying to get to the end of the line cos that's where she thought she should be. In the end she was somewhere in the middle. When we had finally got ourselves sorted we had to say our house numbers out loud to make sure that we had done it properly. It started okay with two and six but then it was Samantha's turn. Samantha said fourteen then Eli said that that was wrong and Samantha said that it wasn't wrong and she should know how old she is. Then Eli said that we've done ages and now we're doing house numbers. "Oh," said Samantha not from number fourteen. Then the instructor asked her what house number she was. "Three hundred and sixty-three." She should have been sent home straight away, instead we all groaned as Samantha had to work her way past everyone up the beam to the far end (apart from Laura who insisted that names beat numbers and so now was so far up one end of the beam that she was almost off it). Then Samantha had a meltdown. She looked at Eli and said, "I don't know why I should keep quiet about you being sick in my tent last night". So Eli had to go home after all.

At lunch we were told that in the afternoon we were going to do a Cresta Run. However, when we turned up at the site we found that there was no snow, just a track made out of decking. Still, it was good fun going down the slope in sledges even though they had wheels and it kept us entertained for several hours.

After dinner we played a game of Scavenger A-Z. We had to go and fill a carrier bag with twenty-six things, one for each letter of the alphabet and we were told to use our initiative. We weren't allowed in the leaders' tents or any other tents, apart from that we could go where we wanted. Team Alex was doing really well and I thought that we would probably win. We found an acorn, then a cereal bowl which we decided could be b or c. Then we decided it could be both b and c. Then we got a stick that could be b for branch so c became cereal bowl. After about half an hour we had everything apart from z. We went back to the messy tent and waited for everyone else to return - I was a bit surprised to find that we had been beaten back by a team led by a girl called Shanice who didn't seem to have much in her bag. Touchy said we could have had Zoe but I said that she wouldn't fit in our bag which he said wasn't important so we had nothing for z so we were going to get a few points deducted. We got twenty-four points. We got twenty-six points for the alphabet, minus one for no z minus one for using b for branch and t for twig as well. No points deducted for late return as we returned in time. We were well winning when it came to Shanice's turn. She opened her bag and tipped out a phone. P for phone. That was it as far as I could see her team had got. One point for p for phone, minus twenty-five for all the other letters. Clair said that it was very good "...as far as it goes, but where's the rest?" Shanice said that the phone was the rest and then said, "A phone, B T phone, Cordless phone, Dead phone, Electric phone, Fone, Grey phone, Heavy phone, I-phone, Jolly phone, Cool phone with a K, Light phone, My phone, New phone, Old phone, Phone, Quiet phone, Red phone, Shanice's phone, Telephone, Useful phone, Very useful phone, Wet phone, Xenophobic phone, Your phone and Zit" as Shanice lifted up her arm and squeezed a white, pussy spot. Clair said, "Twenty-six points for the alphabet, plus fifty for initiative gives seventy-six points. So Shanice's team wins and her phone is confiscated cos no phones on camp." I told Clair that that wasn't using initiative, it was cheating and Clair said that I could use my initiative on another occasion and maybe I could win. So I will and I will.

Around the camp fire with hot chocolate Marculf suddenly stood up and said, with a big smile on his face, that he was gay. I don't know why he's so happy about it. Now no one will want to share a tent with him now. And neither will they have to as far as I'm concerned.

### Saturday 1st August
### Skip
Clair suggested that the Scouts play a game of A to Z Scavenger hunt this evening with extra points for initiative. This meant that we could all have a sit-down with a coffee for half an hour's peace. It wasn't to be. We sent the Scouts off and within two minutes Sarah-Jane came running out of the mess tent saying (although it was Sarah-Jane so she was probably whispering but it came out as shouting), "Don't worry, we'll clear it up in a minute." I looked at Clair and she looked at me. We put down our coffees and ran over to the tent and found C for cereal or Coco Pops all over the floor. It was quite a mess, being an industrial size cereal box which was by now almost completely empty. "Never mind," said Clair and we cleared them up as best we could, back into the box. "I'll clear up the rest and throw them away in the morning, when we can see what we're doing. Anyway, someone's moved the dustpan and brush. Eli had it last night, that's all I know."

Just as we were going to send the Scouts off to bed, Marculf decided to tell the Scouts that he was gay. This was a very strange thing for a twelve year old boy to announce and was probably going to have ramifications, so I asked to have a little word with him once the others were going off to bed. I asked him quietly and with the look of a concerned parent if he were sure he was gay because we can deal with it. He said that he was certain as he had never been on camp before and then said, "It's so much fun!" "What, being gay?" "Yes, Skip. It's just so much fun with the hot chocolate and the Cresta Run and being able to stay up late." He disappeared and returned a minute later with his dictionary. "Look," he said. He read out, "'Given to pleasure'. That's what I am." "I'm given to reading your dictionary," as I reached out for it. It was a Cassells's Concise English Dictionary from 1924. I told Marculf that "gay" meant other things now. "Like what?" "Like, it doesn't matter. Just go and tell the other Scouts that you're given to pleasure."

When we had finally managed to get all the Scouts into bed I found the dustpan and brush under a table. I must remember to tell Eli to put things back where he finds them. I swept up the rest of the Coco Pops and put them in the box. Now I can put them on the camp fire tomorrow evening. They'll make quite a blaze!

### Saturday 1st August
### Late
### Alex
Marculf has just stuck his head in our tent and told us, "I'm given to pleasure." Eli shouted out, "What, like a Cresta Run?" Too late, he was gone. That was a narrow escape.

### Sunday 2nd August
### Alex
This morning I showed my initiative as I had lost my bowl

(cereal) as it had been used in the A to Z game then it disappeared. I got up early and went into the messy tent. I found the Coco Pops and took the whole inside pack out of the cardboard box. The wax bag that keeps them from going soggy is quite strong so I got some milk and poured it into the bag, folded over the top, held it firmly and shook it. I then sat down and started to eat them. At least I had my spoon. Then Aaron came in. "Cool," he said. "There's an idea for when we're on a backwards camp. That's where no pots and pans are allowed." So now I know. It is a bit backwards if you ask me, when there are loads of pots and pans around. However, Aaron is a friend and there was no one listening so I asked him why it was called "backwards." He looked at me as if I was stupid and said, "Back - WOODS. Like in the middle of nowhere with only trees." When I then asked him what backwards cooking was then he said, "That's when you get the Haribos first, then the hot chocolate. Then you have ice cream, then spag bol and you start (or finish) with the soup." This is a great idea. I always think it's silly that I get full on boring stuff then I have no room for the fun stuff at the end. Why can't we have the fun stuff at the beginning and then only have the boring stuff if we have room? I told Aaron not to tell anyone and he said, "Anyone tell won't I, okay that's. That's a backwards sentence, tee, hee!" I like Aaron. Not like I like Tegan and not like Marculf likes Aaron (possibly) but he's quite fun. I asked him if he would like some of what was left of my backwoods cereal but he didn't. I got to the bottom of the bag and swigged the remains of what looked like chocolate milk shake. Didn't taste like it though. When Clair came in I told her that I had my cereal with no cereal bowl and cos she looked as though she didn't know what to say I reminded her that I had used my initiative. "Although," I told her, "the bottom of the packet tasted like mud." "That's because it probably is," she said, smiling. "Ha, ha, Clair," I thought. "I'm not that stupid. Why would anyone put mud in a Coco Pop packet?"

No one talked to Marculf at breakfast so when we were washing up Skip had to tell us that Marculf wasn't gay, he was just full of mirth (whatever that is). This was a relief as no one had wanted to share a canoe with him, apart from Laura. Barnaby reckons that the only reason that Marculf told everyone that he was gay was so that none of the boys would share with him, and then he could share with Laura and not with one of the boys. If this is true it's a very smart move so I thought that I would tell Skip that I was gay as well so that I could share a canoe with Sarah-Jane. I wasn't going to announce it to the world so after we had washed up I went and told Clair that I was gay. She asked me how long I had known this and I told her since breakfast but when she looked a bit puzzled I told her that it was okay cos it would probably have worn off by teatime. Then she sighed and said that in that case it was probably best if I didn't tell anyone else.

After breakfast we had a practice with the kayaks in the lake like we're going to use in Italy and the canoes like we're going to use in France to go down the Ardeche which is a river. To get us used to using the kayaks at speed we played a game of Fishy, Fishy. Skip was the shark and he had to shout, "Fishy, fishy, come swim in my sea." We then had to all shout, "Sharky, sharky you can't catch me!" We then had to paddle from one side of the bank to the other without Skip tapping the front of our kayaks three times. I didn't last long as I was very keen not end up in the lake, being nibbled by the piranhas so I allowed myself to be caught. I then had to team up with Skip so that we were both sharks. It went on like this until there were no fish left. Barnaby won because he went and hid in the reeds, but our instructor went and got him out and then capsized his boat with Barnaby in it. I'm glad I wasn't the last fishy.

Then we had a go with the canoes. We had two each in an open-topped canoe and a paddle each. I had Eli in mine. I told him that I was gay until teatime so he just said "cool" and sat at the back of the canoe. This is where the heavier and more experienced person is meant to sit. This means me (more experienced) but I didn't say anything. Aaron works as an assistant instructor at Danson Lakes so he knew what to do. He decided to launch his canoe off the edge of the bank and not down the slope. His canoe went in nose first and sank! Fortunately Aaron was in the canoe so he sunk too. He then had to uncapsize the canoe. This is not an easy task with no co-pilot. We then learnt some paddling techniques which will be useful when we go down the Ardeche and then we all had to capsize the canoes so that we knew how to get them all uncapsized. I told the instructor that I didn't want to capsize mine as I didn't want to get eaten by the piranhas but he told me that I had to so that I would know what to do on the Ardeche when (note, not if) I capsize as it is far more dangerous in the Ardeche as there are crocodiles. So I did capsize my boat although I wasn't very happy about it and Aaron helped me uncapsize it. By now I had Laura in the boat cos Eli had decided he didn't want to get back in with me after we had capsized so he swapped. Then Laura just jumped in the lake cos that's what you have to do in the Ardeche when you get too hot. She just kept smiling and saying that the water was lovely and warm and all the while I knew that her toes were being eaten.

When she finally got back in the canoe I found that her toes hadn't been eaten so she had had a lucky escape.

In the afternoon we did raft-building. We were put into teams and each team was given four huge plastic drums and six big sticks that are called staves. We also had twelve lengths of rope. We had to use this stuff to build a raft to get us from one side of the lake to the other without being eaten by piranhas. Skip had told us that every lashing starts with a clover hitch so we could do that but then it got a bit more difficult with trying to make the drums stay in place, but we did okay. Barnaby had to go and ask for more rope because he had someone called Ayoub on his team who Barnaby said was a bit of a pain so the first thing that Barnaby did was lash him to a tree which used up most of his rope. But he started and finished with a clover hitch so he'd done it quite well. Aaron had to ask for more drums and he made a really big raft as he said that the more drums, the more bouncy. When it was time to lunch the rafts my team was the only one that stayed afloat without breaking up into little pieces. This is probably because Skip had showed us how to do good lashes. Aaron decided that he wouldn't try and carry the raft to the slipway. (Note for the future, make sure that we build the raft near the slipway). Aaron decided instead to lunch his raft off the side of the bank. That meant a one metre drop off the edge. Aaron hadn't lashed any of his drums to the staves. They pushed the raft off the edge and it went head-first into the lake, did a handstand, turned over and all the drums went bobbing away around the lake. Fortunately Skip had made sure that no one was on the raft when it was being lunched otherwise they would have been squashed. Or drowned. Or eaten. Then Skip said that Team Mad Macs had to go into the lake to get all the stuff out.

Tegan said that Aaron could borrow our raft (I wouldn't have let him) and off they went. Then Barnaby appeared. He jumped into the lake and swum up to our raft and got out his penknife (he said that he was allowed a penknife when raft-building cos it was waterproof). He then cut the lashings. The staves didn't stay, they floated away and so did the drums and Aaron's team ended up in the water being eaten. By now Ayoub had been freed and his team (minus Barnaby) had made their raft. It was lunched quite successfully but then when it got halfway across the lake Aaron tried to climb on board using the kayak way that we had been taught. He grabbed the raft as far over as he could but instead of pulling himself on board he pulled out the middle stave and the raft fell apart and Ayoub's team (minus Barnaby who was already in) all went in and were eaten. The only other raft left that worked was one that Eli made. It was a one man raft which he had made by lashing four staves in a rectangle and then lashing one drum on top. He then launched it and got on the drum with his feet on the stave frame but he was so high up he couldn't reach the water to paddle. This didn't stop him from trying to rent out his one-man raft for ten pence for ten minutes but by this time he was too late. EVERYONE was in the water and Touchy had brought a mobile water cannon and so everyone was soaked, even the leaders, and all the barrels were in the water and all the staves and most of the rope was at the bottom of the lake being eaten by the piranhas.

When we had finally got all the drums and staves out of the lake and some of the rope we went and had a shower, counted our toes and then had tea. And what was on the menu? Tuna fish sandwiches. Well, I suppose Thriftywood lake has a ready supply of big fat fish in the lake, what with all those toes that are eaten during raft-not-building.

At the end of the camp, because we had all done so well, Clair gave us all a Thriftywood badge for our badge blankets apart from the cool corner who were also given badges but theirs said, "Can't be bothered" which made them all smile but I bet they'll be bothered when their mummies are sewing their badges onto their badge blankets and they get asked why they have been given that badge and then they'll be in big trouble cos their daddies have paid lots of money for the France Italy trip and if they can't be bothered then they might as well not be bothered in Bromley (cos I don't think any of them live in Chislehurst cos everyone's bothered in Chislehurst) which is a lot cheaper than can't be bothered in France Italy.

## Sunday 2nd August
## Skip
"You're a happy girl, aren't you Laura?" I said to her during breakfast. "Yes," she said. Then she added, without pausing for a breath, "Except for when my lovely chubby hamster died." "Oh dear, when did your hamster die?" "Two hundred and seventy-six days ago," she said, and burst into tears.

Once all the Scouts had left, all that remained was the clearing up. There was not a lot to do apart from hoovering up the rest of the Coco Pops and then to have a general wipe down of the tables. Whilst I was over in the too-cool-for-school corner I found five "Can't be bothered" badges. They will be so disappointed so I've brought them home and will post them to them in the morning.

## Friday 7th August

## Alex

France Italy has arrived! We all met in Chislehurst in a car park and got on a really smart coach. It has a side door and when you get on it's like climbing into a space ship as it's all black inside with carpet and stuff. It even has a toilet! Now that's a really good idea. Why don't we have a toilet in our car, then when we go out for the day we wouldn't have to keep stopping (or not stopping although it's needed) cos mummy has told me to drink loads of water so I do and then we have just reached the motorway and I want to have a wee and daddy says that I'll have to wait but I can't wait and so I just burst. I thought that I couldn't wait to go to the toilet and I was going to be first in the toilet. We could sit next to who we like so I'm sitting next to Barnaby cos we had to give our money in to a man called Martin who is a Scout leader who has the camp bank so we don't spend all our money at once. Mummy has given me thirty Euros which I gave to Martin and my passport and my hiccup card so that if I'm ill I will be made better and not just left to die. Barnaby gave Martin three Euros but he kept the rest and not told Martin. Martin asked him if that was all he had, Barnaby didn't lie. He just said that he had a little bit for the ferry and that was okay wasn't it cos he had to eat? Martin said that that was fine. So I asked Barnaby how many Euros he hadn't handed in to camp Martin bank and he said, "Shhh, I'll show you in a minute."

The cool corner from Thriftywood piled on first and tried to get the five seats at the back which meant that they would have to be called something different cos they weren't in a corner any more. But they weren't allowed in the back seats cos that's where the driver sleeps when he's not driving so they all got a bit split up. The first shall be last eh, Chloe?!

The leaders were allowed two seats each which meant that the cool corner had one left over and so cool Ayoub had to sit with Nathan which was not a good idea as Nathan was already holding a sick bag. When the coach started and we had waved goodbye to our mummies, and some of the daddies who don't work, apart from Nathan cos his mummy and daddy are dead, some of the Scouts were crying. I wasn't but mummy was. Graham stood up at the front and said that we had two drivers, one called Harry who is from England and one called Christoph who is from France. I think that two drivers is a bit odd but I suppose that when we get to France Italy they have to change cos maybe Harry is not allowed to drive in France Italy which is a good idea in case he drives on the wrong side cos Marculf said that everyone in the world drives on the right side, which is the wrong side, apart from England where we drive on the left side which is the right side, sort of. Graham is a Scout dad who has just come along with his son, but he seems to think he's a Scout leader which he isn't. He's still a bit of an ASL though.

Then Graham stood up again at the front and said over the speaker thing that on this trip it would be almost impossible to drink too much water or to put on too much sun cream. He then said that we weren't allowed to be sick in the sink in the toilet and we had to use a sick bag. He also said that we couldn't go to the toilet on the coach which was a bit silly cos why was there a toilet on the coach if we couldn't use it? Maybe it was just for the leaders cos maybe they need it more, but Scouts need to wee as well. Anyway, I didn't use it and no one else did and when we got to Dover we got on the ferry and I went to the toilet on the ferry cos that was allowed. No one stopped us at Dover and Clair had all our passports ready but the English passport people just waved us through and so did the French people so we didn't really need our passports at all.

Tegan and Ethan had been to New York recently and had brought back some jelly beans but they weren't ordinary jelly beans. They were paired off (the jelly beans) so that any one colour and pattern could taste really nice or really disgusting. The worst ones were the white ones with different colour spots. They could be tutti frutti or smelly socks. The other ones that were really disgusting were the brown ones. These could be chocolate or dog food. There was also peach or sick.

We weren't allowed outside on the ferry without a leader so if you hadn't given all your money to Martin you could go and spend some in the shop cos that was inside. Barnaby had his money hidden in a secret pocket in case Martin searched him so he bought some ice cream. Hugo had some money as well. This wasn't really very fair cos all he had to do was ask his dad and not bother with camp Martin bank.

Most of us had something to eat. I had a burger with chips and I asked for it in French so I said, "Un burger avec, er, chips, s'il vous plait" and the French man said, "Sure" like he sounded very English but he understood my French so he was French but cos he must spend all his life going backwards and forwards between England and France then he must get used to speaking English. Gosh he must have a lot of stamps in his passport. Hugo bought some after shave but he's thirteen so he probably needs it. Then we got back on the coach. We were supposed to all meet by the information desk but Aaron was missing so Skip got the captain to put out an announcement that went all over the ship. It went, "Ding, dong. Would Aaron xxxxx make himself known to a staff member immediately?" Then we had to all go down to the coach while Skip looked for him. When Skip finally arrived back with Aaron Graham asked where Aaron had been and Aaron said, "Mind your own business," and Graham didn't say anything. Aaron then walked straight into the toilet without asking anyone and nobody said anything so why didn't he go on the ferry? When he reappeared we asked him how he managed to get lost on the ferry. "I didn't get lost," he said. "I was avoiding the riff-raff." I bet he was in the drivers' lounge. We then trundled (last) off the ferry. It was getting dark and Barnaby said, "Let's go in the toilet," and cos Touchy who was on patrol in the seat opposite the entrance to the toilet was snoring and cos we were opposite the toilet steps I told Barnaby we need to be really quiet cos Touchy was on look out duty. So we tiptoed down the steps and went in. It was really small. Barnaby got out his phone and said that he was going to text his mum. I couldn't believe it! The kit list said, as it always does, "no phones" and Barnaby's got his. Barnaby said that it was for emergencies and James would always have his phone, even on Everest. Anyway, he said that no one's going to know and I wasn't going to tell so I asked him what he wanted a phone for in the toilet cos I had no idea. But he just giggled and said, "Sometimes you have to do things in secret that no one needs to know about." It all sounded a bit spooky. I wondered whether it was really a gun or a knife. Barnaby then told me that he really was going to text his mummy. I was already missing my mummy so I said that when he had finished could he text my mummy as well, for me? When he asked me what he wanted me to say I told him that he just needed to say to her that I loved her and that I missed her. Then he laughed which wasn't very nice. When I asked him what was so funny and wasn't he going to tell his mummy the same thing he said, "Fat chance! I'm going to tell her about the peedo in our midst." I had no idea what he was talking about so I said to just tell my mummy the same and I told him the number. Mummy taught me her mobile number cos she said that you would never know when you might need it. This was definitely one of those times.

There was no room to do a wee in the toilet and if you wanted to do a poo then you probably would have to stand on the toilet seat and sort of crouch down although there was a sign on the wall that said, "Please do not open your bowels in the toilet." Barnaby said, "What do you think that means?" I think it means don't poo in the loo. If so, this is a bit odd. Where do they think that we should poo? I thought that maybe we should have brought our Scout chemical toilet and stuck it in the hold with the luggage and I bet there's a way down there from inside the coach like down a fireman's pole or something like that. Barnaby sat on the toilet seat and I sat on the sink. Then Barnaby showed me his Euros and he said that he had over two hundred which is like a thousand pounds and he said that I mustn't tell anyone. Then he showed me what he had bought in the shop on the ferry and the box said that it was Clarains Instant Smooth Self-Tanning. Barnaby said that you put it on your face and it looks like you are from Essex where there is loads of sun and so he opened the jar and it was creamy stuff like vanilla mousse only you can't eat it. He took out a huge handful and wiped it all over his face. He looked like he had been hit by a creamy snowball. Then he gave the jar to me and I put the rest on my face and then someone knocked on the door. And so Barnaby put the jar in the bin. Well he couldn't have put it down the toilet cos if we can't poo down there I've no idea what might happen if we put a glass jar down there. It might get into the engine and the coach would break down. We opened the door and it was Graham and how did he know we were in there cos he was sitting at the front of the coach? He asked us what we had been doing and Barnaby said, "Nothing," and he got cross and said, "Have you been going to the toilet?" and we said no cos we hadn't and then he got more cross and said what were we doing if we weren't going to the toilet? Barnaby said that we hadn't been removing our bowels, definitely not. (Barnaby hadn't read the notice properly). Graham said that he would hope not otherwise we would have to go straight to A & E. Barnaby then told him that we were in France and in France it's SAMU not A & E. Graham look like he was going to blow up so Barnaby said that he was showing me something and Graham asked what it was he was showing me. Barnaby said it was a secret and then Graham told us to go back to our seats. We thought that we were in the clear but as we followed Graham up the stairs Touchy looked at us out of one eye and asked, "What have you got on your faces?" Barnaby said, "Sun cream, like Graham said," even though it had got dark outside. We didn't wait for an answer, we just went back to our seats quickly and put our heads down again. We then stopped at a service station for the toilet and we pretended we were asleep and while everyone was going to the toilet we both used the one on the coach. And we both had a poo. And now we're watching Shrek and Barnaby has just fallen asleep and then we're going to watch something else.

**Friday August 7th**

**Skip**

We had a bit of a traffic delay at Dover and whilst the driver went to get some petrol Martin changed the Sat Nav so that it spoke in French. When we got back on the coach at Calais it started speaking to Harry in French so Christoph said he would translate. We then had to point out to Christoph that that if he spends the whole night translating then we would have no one to drive the coach in the morning. When we got to the first stop we changed it back to English, for Harry at least.

So far everything appears to have gone without a hitch. We did have a slight hold-up at Calais when Aaron didn't meet us at where the Scouts had been told to muster so I had to go for a search having got the purser's office to broadcast a message to make himself available. They asked for my mobile number so that they could text me when he had been found. I was beginning to feel extremely relieved that I had told them not to go outside so that if he had and had drowned at least I was in the clear. With that a message came through to say that Aaron was upstairs in the Club Lounge.

I bombed up the stairs to find Aaron, happy as a sandboy, settling his bill. "Sorry I'm a bit late Skip, but I was enjoying myself too much. It's only a few pounds and you get a bit of peace and quiet, a free drink and a read of a newspaper." "That's great, but we're waiting to go. Have you had anything to eat?" "Yes, but I need to go to the toilet." "Go on the coach. This is an emergency." "Goodbye, Aaron," said the waiters with a wave as Aaron started off down the stairs; one of them gave me his receipt that had been printed off. I had a quick look. What was there on the menu that Aaron hadn't eaten? Inside ninety minutes or so he had polished off a selection of olives, some oriental nuts, a rare roast beef open sandwich, a Cornish cream tea and a glass of Champagne! Back on the coach I wandered down to Aaron after he had been to the toilet and asked him if he had put his cash in Martin's camp bank. "I don't have any cash, Skip," he said, "just a debit card, and he's not having that."

## Saturday 8th August
### Alex
I woke up about five o'clock this morning. There's a clock at the front of the coach above the driver's head and a green light that sometimes goes red. I think that it tells us when the driver is speeding. Well it may be six o'clock cos we've gone forward an hour but I don't know if the driver changed the clock. In France people live for one hour less than in England. That could be quite useful if you want to miss off the last hour of your life with all the gurgling and stuff but I don't think it works that way. It was still dark cos all the curtains were closed but Barnaby was awake and he said that he freaked out in the night. He had fallen asleep during Shrek and woken up and it was Despicable Me and he was really confused cos he thought he was still watching the same film.

Some Scouts were still asleep so I opened the curtain thing quietly and looked out of the window and we were in France as we could see the mountains in the distance. Then I looked at Barnaby and I got a bit of a shock cos he looked a bit like Marculf cos he wasn't white any more. Barnaby turned the little light on above his seat and he had gone ORANGE! And I said, "You've gone orange Barnaby," and he said something I wasn't expecting, "So have you." Touchy was

203

awake and so I asked him cos I didn't want to go to the toilet to look in the mirror even though I wasn't even going to do a wee and I was scared that we had caught something in the toilet and Touchy asked me what I had put on my face. I told him sun cream, agaaain! He was still looking at me a bit oddly so I told him that it was Barnaby's so that he would get into more trouble cos it wasn't looking good at that moment even though the day had only just started. Touchy then asked me if it was medicinal and I said I didn't know but the jar was in the bin in the toilet. Then Touchy got up and went into the toilet but I don't think he was doing a poo or a wee. There was no space for an adult to get into the toilet properly so Touchy had to come out without shutting the door and then he had to go in backwards and then he sat on the toilet seat, so no weeing standing up anyway and if you're sitting down how can you avoid doing a poo? He couldn't even shut the door now. He put his hand in the bin and brought out Barnabys' jar of Clarains Instant Smooth Self-Tanning and then started laughing and then he looked up at us and smiled and said that he thought that he might need the toilet after all. He then told us that it looked like we had a peculiar strain of sifilis. Then he got out and climbed back up the steps but he didn't go and sit down. He went up the front to where Clair and Graham were and I knew that we were going to get really told off so we pretended to be asleep. After a few minutes Touchy came back to his seat and he was still laughing. He leant over to us and said that Skip thought that we may have to go to hospital and be treated for excessive sun exposure but I think he was joking as I'm still here. Then he asked to look at our hands and when we showed him he laughed even more and he then rummaged in his rucksack and got out his special ultra-violet torch and shone it on our hands and they glowed and then he laughed some more so I don't think we were dying. Anyway, Laura was sitting behind us and she asked Touchy where he got such a fab torch from and he said that it was a secret but he could get his hands on any torch cos his name was Torchy.

This was a big relief I can tell you, Mr Diary.

Barnaby then said that he had to text his mum to tell her something important and to ignore his previous text. He then said that he ought to text my mummy as well and I said, "Okay." Perhaps he was going to tell his mummy that he loved her after all. And my mummy. From me that is, not Barnaby. Cos otherwise that may seem a bit odd.

We then had to stop at a service station in France for breakfast. We were meant to bring breakfast but most Scouts don't like to just look at food for more than a few minutes so had eaten it when they were watching Shrek. Even when we were Cubs going on a trip, Akela used to let us have our lunch at about half past nine cos otherwise we would be picking at our packed lunches and asking, "Is it time for lunch yet?" every five minutes so we used to get lunch out of the way as soon as possible. We went in the shop and I went with Barnaby and EVERYONE was looking at us like we were Martians or something and when we went to the till cos Barnaby was buying a fire extinguisher the till lady said, "So you vill be usin' zat to put out yer face coz it iz on fire? Ha, ha!" or something like that. Why she couldn't speak English properly I've know idea. She certainly didn't come from Chislehurst. Maybe she came from Georgia, like Marculf. I asked Barnaby why he needed to buy a fire extinguisher in front of her so that she knew that it would be okay and he said that it was because he didn't have one. This is a bit of an odd reason cos I don't have a nucleer submarine but it doesn't mean I want to buy one. I told him that Skip had loads of old ones at the Scout Hut (fire extinguishers not nucleer subs) and he could probably have one of those but he then said that he was going to put it on his bicycle like you have to have one if you're in your car when you're in France Italy. I don't know if that includes bicycles cos some fire extinguishers are really big. Maybe you could get away with just a water bottle, especially if you painted it red. I can't think that a small fire extinguisher like Barnaby's bought would hold much water though.

Then Barnaby bought a chocolate cross aunt and put it in le microwave (which is the French word for microwave) cos that's what the French people do to warm up their food in shops and he pressed 10.00 minutes instead of 1.00 minutes and the cross aunt first went all flat and then started to smoke and then it was time to go and Barnaby didn't know how to stop the microwave and then the cross aunt caught fire and the till lady screamed and Barnaby pulled the pin out of the fire extinguisher and squeezed the trigger. I thought just a little bit of water would come out but, on no! Tons of foam came flying out like enough to fill the Scout Hut and Barnaby couldn't open the microwave and there was smoke and flames and people were screaming and outside big shutters came down around all the patrol pumps and Barnaby couldn't turn his fire extinguisher off so he just aimed it at the microwave and sprayed and sprayed and sprayed and covered it with foam and Barnaby still couldn't stop the fire extinguisher.

Then Graham appeared.

He asked what on earth was going on and so I said, "Mind your own business," but I think he did have business in this particular situation so I said that Barnaby was putting out a fire in the microwave and then a man with a big moustache and a badge on his suit appeared and he was looking very worried and kept looking at the ceiling. We looked up and there were some red things on the ceiling and they were blinking and peeping and Mr Moustache shouted at another man who had appeared and he had a moustache as well. Mr Moustache (number one) shouted at him, "Alors, les gicleurs, les gicleurs," and pointed prodding at the ceiling and Mr Moustache (number two) ran off. Then the peeping stopped and Mr Moustache (number one) breathed a big sigh and smiled at Graham but Graham hadn't done anything. Graham told Mr Moustache (number one) that Barnaby had put out a fire in the microwave and the man shook Barnaby's hand like he was trying to shake it off. Then Mr Moustache (number one) kissed Barnaby which wouldn't be allowed in England and then he said, "Vait," although Barnaby was ready to run off. Mr Moustache (number one) disappeared off and so we waited and then he came back with a great big enormous tub of aloe vera gel and Mr Moustache (number two) appeared again with TWO huge fire extinguishers like you see on a fire engine and they gave the gel to Graham and told Graham that Barnaby's face was an emergency. Then number one looked at me and then he said to Graham, "And 'im." Then number two gave both fire extinguishers to Barnaby and then he gave him a hundred Euros! Then number two asked Barnaby, "Do you need zee 'ospital?" and Barnaby said, "No, I have a peculiar strain of sawryasis," and number two said, "Oh, sawryasis?" and looked at number one and then number two went away

207

again and came back with a really big penknife and gave that to Barnaby as well. Barnaby just smiled and put it in his pocket. Then number one kissed him AGAIN! but only on his head this time. Then Skip appeared and said that he had only been for a wee and he was covered in water. He said something to number one in French and number one shook Skip's hand and kissed him as well and Skip kissed him back and Skip wrote something on a piece of paper and gave it to the man and then we left. Skip had to carry the fire extinguishers though cos they were too heavy for Barnaby (he has no muscles, apart from in his mouth).

After all this excitement Nathan decided to play it safe. He had bought some microwave porridge in a plastic carton but there was no way he was going to use the other microwave to heat it up. Well, he couldn't have anyway cos Mr Moustache (one or two) had taken it away. So he went and got some hot water from the coffee machine but he pressed the green tea button which made the porridge go a yucky colour so Nathan got lime porridge.

Then there was loads of noise outside and seventeen fire engines appeared cos we counted them and Skip said he thought that it was time to go, like now.

When we were back on the coach we whizzed off quickly while we were still putting our seat belts on and Nathan was then suddenly sick and no one had any warning or heard him but because he was still holding his sick bag from yesterday he was okay and he took it up to Clair at the front of the coach and I thought he had said that he had been sick and Clair probably said that she didn't want it and that he must fold the bag up and put it in the sick bucket at the back of the coach and then Nathan asked Clair for a fork and she gave him a plastic one and then he turned round and started walking to the back of the coach and he opened his sick bag and started EATING HIS SICK! And everyone was screaming and crying and Laura was then really, really sick. But she didn't have a sick bag. She was sick everywhere, over Sarah-Jane and herself and her seat and then the floor and then Nathan sat down and leant over the back of the seat and whispered to me and Barnaby that it wasn't sick in his sick bag it was his green tea button porridge which he had put in a sick bag cos the carton was hot and how was he to know that Scouts would think he was eating his own sick and no one had told Skip and Martin came up and quarantined Nathan at the back of the coach. So Nathan had to go and lie down in the back row and he wasn't allowed to go and talk to Clair and so he had five seats all to himself so he thought that if that was what happens when you're (not) sick then it's not a bad thing at all and Laura, who was really sick had to go and sit in the toilet which is probably the worst place that she could have been sent to cos she wasn't allowed to be sick in the sink and she couldn't poo in the toilet. I suppose she could have been sick in the toilet and done a poo in the sink cos no one told her that she couldn't do it that way round. The notice did say about not opening your bowls but it didn't say anything about not opening your mouth. Anyway, all she could smell was Barnaby's tub of orange man vanilla cream and she had to keep the door open and then she was sick again so Barnaby tried to give her a fork and then she cried and said she wanted to go home.

When Skip came up the coach to investigate the noise (and smell), Barnaby asked him what a "les gicleurs" is. Skip told him it meant sprinkler, "like what happened to me in the toilet." Skip didn't look very pleased. Although, had number two not been so quick, I think that the whole coach load of us would have been sprinkled. Actually that would probably also include the whole service station. Still, better to be flooded than blown up.

I wonder what would happen if a patrol station did blow up? First there would be a great big bang and everyone in the patrol station would be blown up and cos it would be an enormous bang they could be blown up miles. Then the patrol would catch on fire in the pipe and I think the patrol comes along a pipe at the side of the motorway from Iran so then the motorway would all be blown up then the port, then the sea, then Germany and places like that and then Iran but they've probably got a tap their end so they can turn it off. Still quite dangerous though.

The coach made some more stops. The first one was soon after the microwave stop but we had to stop quickly cos we had no diesel cos we had to leave in a bit of a hurry and then another stop but we weren't allowed out of the coach unless we were bursting so we all said that we were bursting so we were all allowed out of the coach and while everyone was in the toilet in the service station Barnaby thought that he would go and try his luck with his Fireman Sam hat on (not really, just metaphysically) to see if he could get another hundred Euros cos soon Barnaby would have enough money for his own trip and as it was money that he had earned during the trip then he wouldn't have to put it in Martin's camp bank, not that he'd put any / much in there to start with, so he went and bought a cross aunt and a mini fire extinguisher. Then he couldn't find a microwave to set fire to his cross aunt cos it looked like there was a "Microwaves for Public Use" sign over a table, but no microwaves so he went back to the till lady and asked her if she could warm up his cross aunt and she gave him a funny look and took it from him and put it on a plate and then she went to the back of the counter where the microwave was and it was just sitting on a work surface like someone didn't know where to put it. She opened it up and put the cross aunt in and as she was pressing the knobs she turned round and asked Barnaby, "Ow many secunds?" and Barnaby said, "Ten minutes." Then Janneke (I know her name cos it was on her badge) said, "Ten secunds?" Barnaby said, "No, minutes." and Janneke said, "I know no minutes, 'ow many secunds?" and Barnaby said five hundred cos he couldn't multiply sixty times ten and Janneke said, "Are you suuure?" and Barnaby said, "Yes." So Janneke put the cross aunt in the microwave and pressed six minutes and forty seconds (cos she couldn't multiply sixty times ten either, maybe they don't have school in France, or maybe it's like Barnaby's school) and then she walked off to sort out the other customers. Actually, most of her other customers were the Scouts cos no one had really been bursting and everyone was buying more breakfast. After two minutes and ten seconds Barnaby shouted, "Fire!" even though there wasn't one – yet, and he pulled the pin out of his fire extinguisher and pulled the trigger thing and there no foam just a huge cloud of freezing cold misty air that came out of the fire extinguisher cos it was a different one, one for freezing stuff probably and Janneke smiled and wandered over and said, "Ah, you funny little English boyz! Le disco! Vere is the lasers?!" and Torchy appeared with his rucksack and got out his laser torch and started flicking it on and off through the cloud that was now all over the ceiling of the service station and then Janneke

211

started singing, "Stayin' alive, stayin' alive, a-ha, ha, ha!" and was pointing one finger in the air and then a man in a suit appeared with a badge on but no moustache and took the fire extinguisher away from Barnaby and said, "Allez! Monsieur Orange" and pointed to the door.

We turned around and Graham was there with his hands folded and staring like a very cross adult.

Uh, oh.

And he was looking at Barnaby and saying nothing. As we were leaving Graham said to Torchy, "Can I have a word?" and we got on the coach and put our heads down again even more. Barnaby was now minus twenty Euros and minus a fire extinguisher and minus a cross aunt and then Torchy got back on. The coach worked its way round the fire engines that were arriving but there were only three of them probably cos most of them were back up the motorway at we know where and we glanced across at Torchy and asked him if he was okay cos he looked a bit told off. He whispered that Graham had told him off and said that he couldn't be left in charge of children if he couldn't even manage looking after them if all they had to do was go to the toilet. Anyway, Torchy didn't appear bothered cos he had taken four separate orders for his laser torch and Janneke wanted SIX! and she gave him loads of Euros and an address in the Netherlands which sounds a bit rude. I told Torchy that she was French and he said that she wasn't, she was Dutch and she just worked in France which seems a bit unfair. Maybe we could have given her a lift home cos it may be on the way. Maybe her car has got stuck and she can't leave the patrol station. I hope she'll be okay. At least she can have a disco at night when everyone else has gone home. Barnaby said that maybe Torchy needed an agent and Torchy told him that he needed someone to sell disco equipment not beauty products.

Anyway, at the next stop it was patrol only again and we weren't allowed out of the coach even though we all said that we were bursting and at the next stop it was toilets only and the stop was in the middle of a wood. So all we could spend was a penny or tuppence. That's what Skip said. I've no idea what tuppence is. Probably a Thompson. That's what daddy calls a poo sometimes. We all had to queue up to use just one sit down toilet with a door. There was no men's and ladies' it was just stand ups and a sit down (well, more like a squat down) at the end behind a door so the boys that wanted to do a number one went first followed by the girls (number one and number two) followed by boys number two. However if you were a boy who wanted to do a number one AND a number two you had to do your number one first in the stand ups and then wait to do a number two or wait to sit down and do a number one and a number two together. Of course, if you were a boy and were desperate to do a number one it was best to do that first and then wait to do a number two, but if you weren't desperate it was better to wait cos then you wouldn't have to wait so long to do a number two. I don't think that some of the Scouts realised this. When we got back on the coach and gone five seconds down the road Tegan said that she wanted a poo and Skip said that we had just stopped and Tegan said, "Yeh, but the girls' toilet was broken cos someone had nicked the toilet." Then Skip went and spoke to Clair and then he came back and said that the toilet wasn't broken or nicked, it was just what happens in France sometimes. "You just have to squat and wee or poo down the hole." Tegan made a face and said that she hadn't been sure what she was supposed to do as no one had told her so she had taken her shoes off and put them on the two footprint bits and then pressed the button and her shoes had disappeared down the hole and so she thought that there was no way that she was going to disappear down a hole never to be seen again so she got out and back on the coach and how was she going to get her shoes back cos otherwise her mum was going to kill her when she got home?

Skip stood up at the front of the coach and announced that we were making good time and should be at our campsite by lunchtime. Then the coach went up a very big hill and then there was a huge queue and there was a sign by the road that said in French that there was a two hour wait and Josh should know cos his dad's French. Skip then told us that there was a short delay and Josh told him it was two hours and Skip said that that was silly although he speaks French as well and Josh told Skip that that was what the sign said and he was right cos it did take two hours and we had to pay to go through this huge tunnel and it was thousands of Euros. Skip told us that we were going through Mon Blonk which is a mountain in France Italy. When we came out the other side we were in Italy and we went down the hill. It was like when you go in the Chanel Tunnel in England and when you come out you are in France only the Chanel Tunnel is flatter cos you only go under a bit of water like the Dartford Tunnel only the Chanel Tunnel takes longer cos you go by train and not by car. It's a pity they didn't make the Chanel Tunnel for cars only then you could get to France much quicker. When I'm Chief Scout I'm going to make the Chanel Tunnel for cars only and no trains. Actually there are two tunnels so in the entrance I'm going to put a huge elastic band like on a catapult but for catapulting humans and not stones. Then you can be catapulted to France quicker even than Woodpeckers' go-kart. There would have to be a big cushion in Calais though otherwise goodness knows where you might end up. It was so smoky coming down the hill now that we are in Italy. The Italian people must love their wood burning stoves. We drove past a big sign that said Courmayeur Skyway Monte Bianco. Skip told us that it was a cable car that you could go on to go skiing. Ha, ha! I thought. Who goes skiing in August? I'm not that stupid. The coach continued down the hill and soon we turned off the main road and over a river and into our campsite. As we drove slowly over the river all bubbling and crashing over the rocks, Tegan jumped up and shouted, "Can anybody see my shoes in there?" and we all laughed. All the campsite staff were outside to welcome us so we must have been the only people there cos otherwise who's looking after everyone else? We all jumped off the coach and this nice girl who said that her name was Pumpy waved her arms in the air and said, "Welcome to ABC Adventure Travel! You're going to have an adventure with us!"

I said that some of us on the coach had had a bit of an adventure already and she said, "I can see that!" and giggled.

She then asked me if I came from Essex. I told her that I had been there once camping. Pumpy then told me that she had been to a nightclub in Essex once and met people like me. I can't imagine why someone her age was going to a nightclub for people of my age so I asked her how old she was. She said that she was twenty-three. That's twice as old as I am which is really old. That means that when I'm fifty and have been Chief Scout for over thirty years she will be over one hundred! That's older than my grandad.

We got all our stuff off the coach and then we were shown our tents like at Thriftywood. We had four people to a tent and the beds are like hospital beds but we had mattresses and I am in with Joe and Marculf and Nathan. At home I have a tent with a bed outside so this was a bit weird with having a bed IN the tent but soon we had unpacked like Graham told us to. Well maybe not. He gave us a talk about packing and unpacking our rucksacks which was a bit late cos we had already packed them. We're supposed to put heavy things at the top and light things at the bottom so that when we go on a hike our centre of gravity is higher so we don't fall over, but I don't have any heavy things in my sleeping bag only Scottie Dog, but he's stuffed. Then we have to make sure that all useful things can be reached easily but all the things in my rucksack are useful otherwise they wouldn't be in the rucksack. Then he said that we have to put our sleeping bags at the bottom but my sleeping bag isn't even in my rucksack. While he was telling us all this Skip came into our tent with a suitcase and asked, "Whose is this?" and Graham said, "Mine." Nathan then said that it must be difficult to carry a suitcase on your back and Graham went red and said, "Stupid boy" and walked off. Well, if he wants to be a Scout leader he's not going to get very far if he speaks to people like that. Rucksack lecture over we then unpacked properly. This means unroll your sleeping bag and then tip everything else on the floor and kick it under the bed (apart from Scottie Dog who stayed guarding my rucksack from inside.) We had all brought camping mats but as we had mattresses we didn't need them so we made a big bouncy cushion with them in the middle of the tent. Nathan reckoned that he could jump off his bed onto the camping mats and bounce onto my bed. He climbed up onto his bed and jumped onto the mats but didn't bounce at all. There was just a big crack and Nathan groaned. Fortunately it wasn't Nathan who had cracked otherwise he would be making a lot more noise, or no noise at all if he was dead, so we shoved him out of the way and moved the camping mats. Oh dear! The sluts now had a big broken bit in the middle of the tent. I suggested that we move all the beds into the middle to cover up the hole and walk round the outside instead of the other way round. Joe thought that it wasn't a good idea as in the middle of the night we would roll all over each other's beds in our sleep. Marculf said that he thought that that was a better idea than rolling out of bed. In the end Joe went and found a large pebble which he's pushed under the broken slut to make it look like it's not broken. But it is, and anyone looking at it would see that it is. I hope we don't get sent home. Anyway it's Nathan's fault so I'm just writing this down in case I'm killed white water rafting and mummy is sued for damage to a slut.

There are loads of leaders here. Some have a tent to themselves and some have to share and they also have electricity and a fridge in their tents which is not camping.

After we had unpacked and put our clothes away neatly, ha, ha, we had to go and report to the ABC messy tent. It's like our messy tent only it's bigger like a marquee and made of plastic (like our tents). There I met Pumpy again and she smiled at me. There are lots of leaders. They are all quite old, like over twenty and they all have funny names like

Bendy, Whizz and Night Rate. The men had funny names as well and there is Bagpuss, Planet and Glug. It seems Italian people don't have proper names like in England. They all smiled and are very nice. There was a leader on each table and we're in four groups cos there are thirty of us plus leaders (Scout) and leaders (ABC).

We were starving cos it was two o'clock and we had had no lunch although some of us, mentioning no names, had had two breakfasts, so we all had a wrap each with special wraps for those Scouts who were allergic to something like eggs and nuts and glutens and meat. Then Josh said that he wasn't allergic to egg, he was intolerant like he can't have omelette but a bit of egg is alright but it was too late and so Josh was going to have no egg for the whole of the holiday. This meant that he wasn't going to be able to eat anything. He won't be able to have cake cos that's got egg in it, he won't be able to have quiche cos that's got egg in it, he won't be able to have pizza cos that's got egg on it. He won't be allowed pancakes either. At least he can have ice cream and Champagne and shots.

Then all of a sudden Night Rate came and gave me a hug cos I said that I was the youngest Scout on the camp although I think it was true but I know now that I'm not. The thing is the ABC leaders asked us all one thing about ourselves that no one else knew and we had to whisper it to the leader on our table. After lunch the leaders stood up to introduce themselves and Night Rate said that she had learned a lot of things about my table. She said that I was the youngest Scout and now I'm not cos there are some who are younger (yee, hee) and then she said that I wanted to be Chief Scout when I'm older and the ABC people laughed and I said to them that that was incorrect cos I would like to be Chief Scout now and Graham looked at me as if I was stupid. He won't be Chief Scout ever, that's for sure. He's not even a Scout leader. When it was Barnaby's turn he said that he had put out a fire at a service station and then we all said that we knew that but the ABC leaders didn't so Barnaby told them the whole story and then they all cheered and then they gave him an extra wrap, not as good as a hundred Euros though.

We were allowed to ask questions and so Barnaby asked Whizz who was in charge now and she said that they were but that our leaders were responsible for looking after us as well so now we have loads of leaders looking after us, almost one each and the ABC leaders are the best leaders cos they're not as old (although quite old) and are smiley but I don't know if they could light a camp fire or do first aid or tie knots or read a map and stuff like that like our Scout leaders can. Probably not.

Then Laura put her hand up and asked, "Please, what is the WiFi password?" Whizz said that the Italians don't have WiFi and all the Scouts that groaned then had to put their hands up and Graham said that any Scout with their hand up had to hand in their phones cos they weren't allowed. Then Martin had to say that it was okay, just don't use them. He said that there won't be any time anyway as we had a week of activity planned. Laura then said, "Well, we have sleeping time." And Martin said, "Yes, precisely, that is not Facebook time." And Laura said, "Mum says that I can do Facebook in my sleep" and Martin just said, "Well, there's nowhere in your tent to charge your phones so I wouldn't bother with them."

After our wraps we prepared for our hike up to an old ruin. That's what Pumpy said we were going to visit. We were each given a map like an Ordinance Survey map at home. These are the best in the world Martin said and he should know cos he's probably been around a bit like Skip. I can't read a map very well yet and these maps were very difficult cos there were loads and loads and loads of wavy lines over them, not like at home where there aren't very many. Pumpy came over and sat next to me and she told me that the lines were called contour lines which show the height of somewhere above sea level and there were loads of lines cos we were in a deep valley that was very steep. We then had to take our compasses and set a bearing which I managed. Pumpy showed me how to do this and so I asked her if she was married and she said no. So I asked her if she would like to be and she giggled and asked me if that was a proposal. I didn't know what she meant so I just said, "It may be." Then she giggled some more and gave me a hug. I thought that it was the right time to ask her another question that had been bothering me. So I took a deep breath and I said, "Pumpy?" "Yes, Alex?" "Pumpy, why is your name Pumpy?" And then she went bright red but still giggled and said, "I'll tell you when we're married." And I thought, "Blimey, I've only just met her and she wants to marry me." So I think I'll have to play it a little bit cooler from now on. So I just smiled. Cos what will Chloe think if I come home married?

It was a bit of a trek to the old ruin but it was worth it once we got to the top as we had a good view for miles around. Pumpy doesn't like Nathan cos he told her that how could somewhere be a new ruin so it had to be old so it was just a ruin? I had to tell Nathan that if somewhere was new but then someone blew it up then it would be a new ruin and Pumpy smiled at me and Nathan wandered off. One way we could see the top of Mon Block and the other down a windy valley. The turret bit at the top of the hill had an old iron door that was locked but there was a bit of a gap under the door where the earth had worn away so Laura managed to crawl under the door but then she couldn't get out and was really stuck and so she started to cry. I told Whizz that as she was in charge she would have to rescue Laura and she looked worried and Laura had gone really quiet and everyone was standing round the door and then someone had the idea of putting their camera under the door and doing a sort of selfie but of someone else which is called a picture. This way you could see what was inside and that is what we did. Barnaby had a camera so he held it in his hand under the door and took a photo. When we had a look at it all we could see was a turret with no ceiling. Then Barnaby had another go as obviously Laura wasn't on the top of the turret and he put his camera on video and videoed all round the bottom inside of the turret. Then he looked at the video and there was no Laura and so the Scouts all started to laugh cos we thought that she may have been eaten or something, or disappeared down a huge hole and that's why the turret was locked up.

We were all thinking that maybe we should just leave Laura there cos we were going to be late for dinner when Laura shouted, "Houdini!" and we turned round and there was Laura standing on the ruined wall and Whizz started to cry and Laura said that she had managed to crawl out of a window round the back of the turret. Then Skip got told off by you know who for allowing Laura under the turret door so it's not just the Scouts that get told off it's Skip as well.

And Torchy. Whizz got out her phone and started texting like mad and she said that we just had to wait for the others to come back. I think that they had obviously gone for a walk somewhere but I don't know where they went cos there weren't many places that they could go seeing as we were on top of a hill.

Tegan thought that Whizz needed a sweet so she offered her one of her jelly beans. Whizz said "thanks" and took a brown one and a tutti frutti one, which can be the worst. Tegan explained that they could be tutti frutti or smelly socks, and chocolate or dog food. Unfortunately Whizz got smelly socks and dog food but she thought it was poo cos it does taste like poo and so she was a little bit sick in a bush and then she cried again. I don't know what poo tastes like cos I've never tasted it. I wonder if Whizz has? She wasn't going to get chocolate, that's for sure, after Tegan had licked all the sweets to work out which were the nice ones and then just ate them and left the horrible ones for the Scouts that she didn't like, and Whizz obviously. After all that excitement we marched back down the hill. I thought that Whizz looked sad and so I went to give her a cuddle like I give mummy. I thought that Whizz was a bit of a funny name so on the way down I asked her what is was short for. Whizz then said that her name was really Nadia, but everyone calls her Whizz cos she runs marathons, although at home her friends call her Nads. I can't understand why she can't be called Nadia though cos it's a much nicer name. I'm going to call her Nadia. When we got back to our camp we were a bit late what with having to look for Laura so we went straight into dinner (after we had washed our hands, of course). We were supposed to go to the boys and girls' toilets but they were further away from the leaders' toilets which were probably nicer so Barnaby suggested that we go in the leaders' toilets cos the leaders never washed their hands and were all chatting in the messy tent so Barnaby went in the leaders' toilets and I stood guard outside. Then Glug suddenly appeared with a big spanner and some other tools and asked me what I was doing and I said "nothing" cos I wasn't and I went back to camp for our dinner which was snails and frogs legs. Well, that's what we told Barnaby cos he was very late for dinner and so missed it so had to have soup. In August. Ha ha! WE had Spaghetti Bolognese for dinner which is a British dish and tortoni for pudding which is also British cos it's ice cream. When Barnaby finally appeared in the mess tent Whizz took one look at him and burst into tears – again! I don't know what the problem is, maybe she doesn't like children.

I didn't want to tell anyone that Barnaby was missing cos I would be asked where I had seen him last and I would have to say that it was in the leaders' toilets and then you know who would tell him off, and me probably, so I didn't say anything. Barnaby told me that he heard me talking to Glug so knew that he would be coming into the leaders' toilets and so hid – in a toilet. He didn't know what Glug was doing but he was in another toilet and he was whistling and making lots of noise with some tools and after hours he flushed the toilet and left. Then Barnaby crept out and no one saw him and he told Nadia that he had got lost which was a bit stupid cos there was nowhere to get lost in and Nadia just smiled and went off and came back with soup. Still, it was tomato soup, so sort of Italian seeing as how we are in Italy.

Laura doesn't eat meat so she had chocolate.

This evening we did high ropes which was really scary. Nadia and Glug were in charge. Nadia taught us how to use the safety lines and how to clip and unclip them. We had two each so that we were always clipped on using one. Once we had had a practice I was off first with Graham behind. Nadia was up in the trees with me and she was looking after me but half way round she had to look after Graham cos he freaked out and said that he wanted to get down which wasn't very easy as we were several hundred feet up in the air. Anyway, Nadia talked him round. I know what she said to him cos I was only just in front and had to wait. She said to Graham, "If the little kid can do it you must be able to, otherwise I'll put you in front of him so that he can watch you fail, and you wouldn't like that, would you?" I didn't know what little kid she was talking about. I couldn't see any, but it seemed to do the trick cos off he went again and at the end he was okay although it had taken him about two hours and it normally takes about twenty minutes. Nadia said that I had done really well but that she had the course record cos she had got round in seven minutes (although she had no one in front holding her up, and no one behind having a freak out). Then we asked to have a go on the other high rope course because it had a really long zip wire but we were told that we couldn't cos it wasn't safe enough for us (although it was safe enough for the Italians). Maybe they're not so heavy.

Even so, the one we did was scary enough. I wasn't going to say anything when one of the platforms wobbled a bit, but Nathan did. He asked Glug, "What happens if someone falls off and dies?" Glug replied straightaway, "Lots of paperwork and a load of mess to clear up." Obviously someone has died on the course cos Glug knew exactly what to do. Then I asked Glug who would have to do the clearing up. He looked at Nadia, smiled, then pointed at her and said "WHIZZ!" Obviously Whizz has had to do clearing up before but she didn't look too bothered about it.

Then we went to bed and I should have gone to sleep hours ago but no one has so I'm sitting here in bed writing up my diary whilst Nathan eats all the sweets that he bought in the service stations as well as some warm cheese and some salami that has melted and an egg mayo sandwich that has started to go a bit runny. Now Joe has just said, "Let's have a sack race," and he's stupid cos we have no sacks, but we've got sleeping bags so we're going to have a sack race with sleeping bags round the outside of the inside of our tent.

Hi, Diary, I'm back. We had our sack race which was fun but everyone's all hot now and Nathan's the winner. Anyway, I still can't get to sleep cos all the leaders are outside and talking and it must be almost time to get up for breakfast. Marculf and Joe are asleep. Joe won't wake up because he brought some foam ear plugs that he's stuck in his ears. He was the only one to bring any. He said that he bought them from Tiger for just two pounds and they're bright green and come in their own little box. Marculf and Nathan went off earlier to the tuck shop and Nathan bought some great big fat March mallows which he said would work. He rolled them up into little sosages that he will be able to get into his ears. Then they will expand and make him deaf for the night. He's eating the rest. He's put a white one in one ear and a pink one in the other. There's probably a joke there but I don't know what it would be. This way, he says, he won't get them muddled up. Marculf is having a funny dream cos he is talking to himself but I don't know what he's saying. Clair is outside and she's been complaining about being bitten by mosquitoes. She's in need of some of daddy's homemade sunflower oil and lavender oil combination. I'll give her some in the morning. She could also make dot leaves up like a head band and wear it cos that's what Nathan says is a good idea to keep mosquitoes away. They were all quiet outside for a while, then they all started screaming and laughing. In a minute I'm going to have to get out of bed and go and tell them to be quiet otherwise they'll wake everyone up. This is not fair on the Scouts that are sleeping. This always happens on camp. Trying to get the leaders to stop talking when they should be fast asleep is a nightmare. If they don't get any sleep they won't be able to look after us properly in the morning. I bet when Tim Peake was in space he got a good night's sleep. Otherwise, in the morning when it was time to do a moonwalk he would have to say to the others, "I'm sorry but I can't do the moonwalk today as I'm too tired cos I've been talking all night after I was bitten by mosquitoes." That's what Clair should do to avoid being bitten by mosquitoes – she should go into space. Bit more expensive than some of daddy's homemade sunflower oil and lavender oil combination though. I want to be an astronaut when I'm Chief Scout. I don't think any Chief Scouts have ever been into space. Bear Grills has been in a helicopter but I don't think it's been up high enough to call it space. Probably it's just been into air.

Oh, this is stupid. I can't get any sleep. I'm going to go and speak to Clair. The leaders need more sleep than this.

**Saturday 8th August**
**Skip**

At midday we finally made it through the Mont Blanc tunnel, over ten kilometres in length and with a long gap in front and behind as vehicles are now staggered through, no longer tail to tail as before the fire in 1999 that led to thirty-eight deaths.

Whereas we entered in France we exited in Italy, above the popular ski resort that is Courmayer. We were so high up that the coach was shrouded in cloud. We trundled down the Aosta valley and passed the Skyway, which whisks skiers halfway up Mont Blanc.

We drove into the top of the Aosta Valley with green vegetation clinging to steep mountains on either side which brought to mind last year's trip to Croatia when I had stayed on the island of Brac which is a bit like the Spanish coast must have been before the advent of mass tourism. An island of stone, with crumbling buildings, even in the middle of lively and well-populated fishing villages it was now like driving up to Dol, in the middle of nowhere. Dol was nestled in its own valley and as I drove into the village I stopped and, being after two o'clock, decided that lunch was in order. I parked up and stumbled across the restaurant Toni and feasted on "mixed meats," which included a spicy sausage, liver, pork, lamb and a bit of chicken. Afterwards, I had walked up the bottom of the valley to the village's second restaurant, and then climbed the winding road up the side of the village where I found a castle, Kastil Gospodnetic, which contained a restaurant offering local food and wine. A member of the Gospodnetic family appeared, a young woman dressed in a simple black dress. She invited me in and, being quiet after the lunchtime session, asked if I would like a tour of the building, which I gratefully accepted. I was shown the downstairs restaurant with the most enormous barrel of wine on display and a grape press for a bar. I then went upstairs to the main living area and guest room, with decoration and furniture unchanged for over one hundred years. The young lady told me that the castle, a valuable and unique example of civil engineering, had been owned by the same family for over three hundred years. I went on my way and climbed still further. Above the village I looked down, a long way down, to the wide valley floor, stretching its way down to the Adriatic at Postira. This could have been the Aosta Valley although Brac's vegetation is mostly its one million olive trees whereas the Aosta Valley's seems to be mostly castles. Furthermore, Dol's valley was only about five kilometres long whereas the Aosta Valley winds its way down to Naples. In the summer there is no river at Dol, but as we reached the Aosta valley floor we came across a raging torrent of a river, the Dora Bella, spewing up mud as it thundered down from Mont Blanc with the melting snow and summer rainfall ending up one hundred miles away in the Po River. I wouldn't want to fall in that by accident; I could end up in Naples. Anyway, I digress. It's just such a lovely part of the world, as is Dol, and we've only just arrived. I'm sure the Scouts will soon be drinking in the culture.

Having said that, Alex appeared a short while ago and told Clair that to avoid being bitten she needs to wear a wreath of doc leaves so now she's sitting outside the mess tent painting her nails but otherwise doing a passable imitation of Julius Caesar. Now Alex has appeared again and told us all to go to bed even though it's only half past ten! I was tempted to tell him that the ranging torrent of a Dora Bella river outside the campsite was the one that we would be white water rafting down. That would've shut him up. But I didn't. Coward!

## Sunday 9th August
### Alex

We woke up really early this morning. All we could hear were the birds singing (in Italian obviously) and Skip shouting, "Petit dejeuner est prêt!" which is Italian for "Breakfast is ready!" according to Laura, who's clever although she doesn't eat meat. Girls aren't allowed in the boys' tents. This is cos girls smell funny, according to Joe, and if there's too much perfume in a boys' tent then Graham would wonder who's been visiting, but Laura doesn't have perfume on so she allowed in (by us that is, no one else knows). Probably the other girls know, unless she's told them that she gone to the toilet, but girls normally do that together so she's probably just sneaked off. Boys aren't allowed in the girls' tents either. This is because boys definitely smell, but not of perfume, except Peter, but he's not here. All of the tents, as well as the leaders, are in a huge rectangle, all facing in, with the messy tent in the corner, so everyone can see who's going in and out of all the tents, but they're quite close together and high so it's really easy to walk round the back without anyone seeing. Laura's tent is four tents away from ours down one side and Graham is next to us on the other side. He has a tent to himself. Skip says that this is cos he snores. The ABC leaders don't sleep with us. They have their own area at the end of our rectangle, behind a wire fence. This is probably in case they try to escape. There are also some families staying here but they have their own camp and they don't do their own washing up so that's not much of an adventure or a camp. Also, Planet said, they get wine with their meals so they'll probably be drunk by the time breakfast's over.

Laura said that yesterday she was playing hide and seek (although no one appeared to have been playing with her). She said that she was squatting behind her tent when she discovered that it had a zip at the back. They all have one! The zip is on the inside with a cover over it, so it's quite well hidden but Laura said that if you're outside and hook your finger under the zip and pull slowly then you can lift the zip up and can get in. It's probably supposed to be an emergency exit but Laura is using it as an emergency entrance. Well, not so much an emergency, more secret. But anyway, she came in and sat on my bed and I knew it was her cos she said it was her. I suppose it could've been someone else cos I still had my eyes closed, but it sounded like Laura although I couldn't smell if it was her. She told us that Shanice was going to get into so much trouble because she had packed her rucksack by herself. I explained that that was a good thing as we were being given responsibility but Laura told us more. She said that Shanice had used the kit list but had only packed one of everything and now she has no clean anything. I can't see why this is a problem so I told Laura that all she had to do was spray perfume around the tent and then everyone would smell okay.

We were trying to whisper but not very well so Nathan and Joe woke up. Joe said that his mummy had laminated his kit list so that it wouldn't get muddy or disintegrate. This is a good idea. Well done Joe's mummy! Joe and Nathan both said how fab their ear plugs were. Joe pulled his two little ones out of his ears, licked them and put them back in their box. Nathan pulled his March mallows out but they were really sticky and so he had loads of yuck stuck to his ears and hair. He put his back in his March mallow bag. It looked like he had pulled out half his ear with them. The white one was white with brown waxy blobs on it and the pink one was the same only it was flat where Nathan had been sleeping on it. He said that they were fine as he was only going to be putting them back in his ears at night time. Laura disappeared out of the back of our tent and so it was time to get up. We pulled our clothes out from under our beds until they were all in one pile in the middle of the tent then sorted out what we were going to wear. Marculf was still fast asleep so we left him in bed and went off for breakfast. On the way to the messy tent, Nathan was attacked by some huge wasps and he ran screaming into the messy tent with the wasps following.

Marculf didn't come to breakfast and so Graham went to wake him up. Graham wasn't allowed in our tent on his own cos he's an adult so he had to stand outside. He was shouting Marculf at the top of his voice and then came back to the messy tent and told us that it was ridiculous but he wouldn't wake up so then I had to go with Graham so that he could go into our tent. I was going to take Joe with me but I said to Graham that I would bring Josh cos Josh isn't frightened of Graham. Nathan wouldn't come in case he was attacked again by the wasps wanting their breakfast. I unzipped our tent and Graham went in and then went mad. He looked at me with big starey eyes and said that we had only been in our tent one night and already it was like a sweary rubbish tip. I was just about to cry but then Josh said to him that he wasn't our Skip and if he didn't apologise to me then he would tell his dad and his dad was, "Ard!" Josh said it with big starey eyes back only he looked even more scary than Graham so I'm glad he wasn't looking at me.

Graham then looked at Josh and spoke like a chav and he said, "Oh yeah, so how hard's your dad, then?" Josh said, "Ard enough to be in prison for gee-bee-ache," and then Graham said, "Let's concentrate on Marculf, shall we?" Graham walked over to his bed and then said without looking up, "What's in his ears?" I told him he had bought some ear plugs from a sweetie shop. Graham grabbed Marculf's shoulders and shook him gently. Marculf opened his eyes and Graham imitated pulling something from his ears whilst looking at Marculf with his starey eyes. Marculf tried to pull his ear plugs out but couldn't so Graham went off to find an ABC leader and told us to stay in the tent. On the way out Graham put his hand into Nathan's bag of March mallows and took one out and put it in his mouth. I hoped it was an ear plug one cos they were about the only ones left. That'll teach him! He came back a minute later with Planet and said that Nathan had told him that Marculf had used chewing gum for ear plugs and at least Nathan had managed to pull his out. I explained to Graham that Nathan hadn't used chewing gum but had used March mallows. "Yeah," said Josh. "And you've just eaten one of them so now Nathan's going to have to sleep on one side all night. That or keep swapping his one ear plug over, which isn't going to work cos he's going to be asleep." But Graham wasn't listening. He went outside the tent and was promptly sick. "Yee, har!" said Josh. "We'll have to send him home. Shall we get Clair to ring his parents?!" Even Planet smiled.

We left Marculf to get dressed and Josh and I went to start / finish our breakfast. Most of the other Scouts had finished already so we had what was left and there was loads of it. We had eggs and bacon and hash brownies. We sat with Planet and Night Rate. Planet is my new friend. I told him that I loved hash brownies. I had never had them before. Planet said that that was just as well and laughed. I like Planet but he thinks he's a girl cos he wears eye liner. I asked him if he wanted to be a girl, but then Night Rate said that he wants to be a rock star. She asked me what I wanted to be and I said I want to be Chief Scout. I don't know of any Chief Scouts who have had eye liner. I don't expect Planet will be Chief Scout. Planet has loads of bracelets on his ankle. I asked Night Rate after breakfast why he wears loads of bracelets round his ankle. (I didn't bother to ask why he wears bracelets cos that's probably what rock stars do.) Night Rate said that it means that when he puts on his wet suit it covers them up. If he had them round his wrist then it wouldn't. I thought that that was very clever. Then Night Rate said that he has his watch round his ankle as well. This isn't so clever. I told Night Rate that that was silly cos every time someone asked him the time he would fall over. Unless he was sitting down. I shall make sure that if I ask Planet what the time is that he's sitting down first.

I went back to our tent to get daddy's special sunflower oil and lavender oil combination. Then I found Clair and gave it to her and said that it was for mosquitoes, like to stop them, not to feed them. Then she smiled at me and said that I was being very prepared. I hope that she likes it.

After we had all washed up we had to all meet in the messy tent for a briefing. All except Marculf. Planet said that Marculf's ear plugs had gone solid and he couldn't get them out and didn't want to damage his ear so Marculf will have to go to hospital. Just for trying to get to sleep.

At the briefing we were told what we were going to do,

which was gorge jumping in a waterfall which was going to be so much fun. We had to go to the stores and get a wetsuit, a helmet, a bouncy aid and then we had to put our shorts on over our wetsuits so that we didn't wear our wetsuits out when sliding down the rocks. All we needed apart from this was a t-shirt and a pair of old trainers which was on our kit list. Pity about our shorts though cos they were going to get worn out instead. Leigh was the youngest Scout leader in our group and he had never put on a bouncy aid before cos he didn't realise that you put it over your head and your arms through the holes either side of the head hole so he put his on like a nappy and everyone laughed - apart from Graham. Nathan was wandering around with his trainers in his hand cos he said they didn't fit him. Skip asked him why he had brought trainers on camp that didn't fit and he said that the kit list said that he had to bring old trainers. Skip looked up at the sky and said, "Yes, old trainers because they're going to get messy, but they've still got to fit you." We then jumped on the coach and headed for the mountains. After about half an hour of going back up the hill we turned left up a windy round. It looked like we were going into the middle of nowhere when all of a sudden we came into a village with a huge big car park. The coach parked and we all jumped off. We put on our wetsuits and stuff and then we had to walk through the village looking like penguins. We stopped at a cafe and then the ABC leaders said that the waterfall was too dangerous due to loads of rain but we could go and have a look at it. First we were allowed a hot chocolate or an ice cream. Then we walked for miles and had a look at the waterfall and then we came down again and got back on the coach and went back to the camp. So that was all a bit dull but at least we got a hot choc. I asked for a hot choc. cos I was a bit chilly cos we were halfway up a mountain somewhere and the waiters asked, "Speciale?" cos that means, "Special" and I said "Yes" cos I was first and I was standing with Skip. Then the hot chocolate girl made it with REAL chocolate that she melted and then chocolate sauce and it was really thick and then that spray cream stuff and then small March mallows and then a shot of cream de menthe and Planet said, "Whoooa!" and I said that it was okay as I liked mint. But Planet said that this mint was a quarter alcohol but I said that it couldn't be wasted so I was allowed to drink it cos Skip didn't see. Then Planet said that any more hot chocolate orders could not be "specials" (apart from his!) and Planet got all the orders in and then I helped take them outside.

When we finally got all the orders sorted and went outside with our drinks, Graham was standing with a mug of hot chocolate (ordinary not special) and he turned to Skip and said, "Why haven't I got one of those?" pointing to mine, not Planet's who had disappeared and Skip said he didn't know and I said he can't have one with alcohol in it cos he's too old. Then he said that he wanted one like mine so he grabbed me by the ear and dragged me back inside and told the waiter that he wanted what I had and he wasn't going to pay any more cos he had been waiting too long. Then he went off to the toilet and while he was in there I said to the waiter to put washing up liquid round the cream instead of cream de mint cos they had some washing up liquid behind the bar that wasn't Fairy but it was the right green colour. Then we all "he, hed" cos they didn't like Graham either then he came out of the toilet and they looked very serious and when Graham walked up to the bar they told him that his drink was ready. He looked at it and said, "That's better" and walked outside drinking it. When it was time to leave I

235

asked Graham whether he liked his hot choc and he said it was quite nice and if there had been time he might have had another. I thought all he needs to do now is drink a glass of water and he could clean his insides out completely cos I reckon they must need doing but I didn't actually say anything at all.

After lunch back at camp, we had to do white water rafting preparation, ready for our adventure on a river tomorrow. Let's hope it doesn't rain when we're doing white water rafting otherwise we will not be able to do this either. We went next door to a white water rafting centre and there they had a big lake for practising on. We had to put on helmets and bouncy aids but nothing else. We didn't need wet suits cos we were going to be getting really wet, not just a little wet like at the waterfall. We then had to get into groups of about eight and get into a big raft. We learnt how to sit on the raft and not in it and then we had to get in if the instructor said, "Get down!" We had to hold onto the rope if the instructor shouted, "Hold!" "Positions" means get back to your seat on the side. We learnt "Right over" which means those on the right have to throw themselves over to the left to bring the raft down if the left side is tipping up, and vice versa. We also learnt how to hold our paddles to avoid losing them or bumping someone on the head. It was quite unbelievable but no one fell in. I think that the thought of having to drink the creamy brown coloured water put everyone off. When our instructor asked if there were any questions I put up my hand and asked, "If there is rain, will the white water rafting be cancelled?" The instructor said, "No, if there's rain then white water rafting will be more fun." Then he laughed, then he laughed a bit more. I didn't laugh. This is serious business. I'd better get plenty of sleep tonight.

When we were in the messy tent after dinner I heard Skip tell Martin that he fancied Clair. This is not something that I wanted to hear. Skip is a married man. I shall tell Skip tomorrow that it is inappropriate for him to fancy another lady.

This evening Nadia and Night Rate had a race on the high ropes and some of us went to watch. Everyone was cheering Night Rate but I wanted Nadia to win. Night Rate went first and everyone was screaming, "Go, Night Rate. Go, Night Rate." When it was Nadia's go, Barnaby started shouting, "Go, Whizz. Go, Whizz." Once he stopped for a bit of air, I started to shout. "Go, Nads," I screamed at the top of my voice, "Go, Nads. Go, Nads." Bendy and Planet looked at me and started laughing at each other. Even Skip was laughing. Maybe they were embarrassed cos they were shouting for the loser. Nadia won and gave me and Barnaby a hug. Barnaby went red. I didn't cos I'm used to getting hugs from old ladies like my mummy and Barnaby isn't.

Everyone's ready for bed now. Joe has put his ear plugs in. Nathan threw his other one away. Marculf has come back from the hospital where he has been for most of the day. He had to have his chewing gum ear plugs removed with a special tool but he had to have an x-ray first but he said that it didn't hurt. I don't have any ear plugs but I think everyone's going to be quieter tonight. I can't even hear Clair outside. Maybe word had got around the Italian mosquitoes that she's not very tasty. Are you listening, Skip?! I told Nathan that Clair's not very tasty and he said, "Well, I would be very worried if you thought that she was, she's at least ninety." I don't know what he's talking about. Sometimes I think that Nathan lives on another planet.

I told Nathan, Joe and Marculf that at least one person had died on the high ropes course and that Nadia had had to clear up the mess. Hopefully it would have only have been a child and not someone like Graham otherwise there would have been a huge amount of mess to clear up cos he probably would've exploded or something. At least he would have clean insides.

Planet alert! Night Rate told me that Planet used to be a Beaver. Judging by the amount of eye liner he was wearing this evening he looks more like a Panda now.

**Sunday 9th August**
**Skip**
Poor old Clair has been suffering from hay fever today and at one point was sitting on a chair outside her tent with her head in her hands and her eyes streaming. One of the other staff walking past saw her and came over. She knelt down beside Clair and said, "I don't know what your friends have said or done but they don't really mean it." She took Clair's hand and said, "Look, this is a happy site and we're all here to make your stay a fun one. If there's anything that we can help you with, just give us a shout in the office. What's your name?" "Clair," said Clair. "Okay Clair, well I'm just going to go and get help – what's your leader's name?" "I am the leader," said Clair through snuffles. Now I know Clair looks young, but there is a limit.

Tomorrow it's white water rafting which is going to be fun. Fortunately we have Javier, who is the main instructor, leading us which is just as well. I did fancy Clair for being the first to fall in; judging by her condition today I think that I'll put money on it.

## Mon 10th August
### Alex

Last night Nathan was really sick. It took him a day to throw up his sweets, warm cheese, salami that had melted and a runny egg mayo sandwich. That meant that it all had a whole day to turn into really horrible sick with the sack race and hike and white water rafting practice and because we had not kept our stuff under our beds thanks to Nathan, Nathan was then sick over all of it. Every night one of the leaders is on sick duty. Last night it happened to be Torchy. Nathan had to go and wake him up and tell him that he had been sick. Then Torchy got us all to move into a spare tent (except Nathan) with our sleeping bags and nothing else. Torchy then moved all our sick stuff outside and put it in a big pile. He then got a bucket of hot water and disinfectant and mopped up the floor as best he could and put Nathan back in the tent and told Nathan that his tent (our old tent) was now the sick tent. Torchy then got one of his flashing red lights and stuck it on top of the pile of clothes like it was some sort of radioactive mound, which actually it probably was. I hoped Laura hadn't tried to visit first thing, otherwise she would have got a shock with just a sick Nathan in our tent.

In the morning Nathan was moved outside on his bed while the ABC leaders deep cleaned our tent so that it was nice and bug free. Then they moved Nathan back in and put a notice on the front of the tent which said, "SICK TENT". Then they took all of our sick clothes away to be washed and

Torchy took back his flashing red light.

During breakfast Graham stood up and said he had two important things to tell us. First he told us that Nathan was in the new sick tent and that no one was to go near it unless they were sick. The second was that no one is to go into anyone else's tent without permission from him, after an unfortunate incident a couple of hours ago. I looked around and everyone had blank faces apart from Laura who had gone really red. After breakfast I followed Laura out of the messy tent and asked her what had happened to make her go red. At first she wouldn't say anything so I asked her if she had been to our tent and found nothing other than a sick Nathan. Then she said to me to come round the corner behind the messy tent where no one could see. Then she said, "It was far worse. I know that you are, or were, the third tent along but when I got up to go to the toilet this morning, on the way back I thought I would come and say hallo, but I forgot that you weren't the end tent. So I went round the back and unzipped the zipper and stuck my head in and do you know what I saw? I saw Graham! And do you know what he was doing? He was sitting on his bed! And do you know what he was doing on his bed? He was doing something that I've never seen a man do before and certainly not a Scout leader! He was covering his face and his arms and his legs with Clarains Instant Smooth Self-Tanning out of a jar just like the one that Barnaby had on the coach only a really BIG jar! Do you think he stole it from Barnaby?" Laura asked with a whisper and this time waited for a reply. I told her that no Graham hadn't stolen it cos we had used all of Barnaby's and that Barnaby's was a small jar and so he must have bought some on the ferry as well. I couldn't believe it! I just had to go and tell Barnaby.

Laura said that Graham hadn't seen her but he looked up as she tried not to giggle and so she ran back to her tent and when she looked later she saw that Graham's tent was all zipped up again so he must've known that something was going on.

When I found Barnaby he was busy helping Planet change some big orange protein gas cylinders. They're called protein gas cos the gas comes with extra bits in it which you can put in your food to make it healthier when you're cooking I think. I told Barnaby what Laura had told me and Planet said that we must leave it to him and smiled. I knew that he was going to do something naughty. He looks like Barnaby, but I don't think that they're related. Of course, if you go back far enough they would be, like great great great great great great cousins or something, but no more than that.

Then it was time to go and die, that is to say, white water rafting. (Well I didn't actually die cos I am writing this, but I didn't know that this morning). Sadly Nathan couldn't come. Still I suppose it was for the best cos the Italian people wouldn't want someone being sick in their river and polluting it with egg sick. We climbed into our wetsuits again, and our helmets and our bouncy aids and got on the coach and went down the valley to a field by a motorway. When we got out we had to walk across the field and then we found some instructors waiting for us with the rafts that we had practised in yesterday. At the edge of the field there was the river bank which was really steep and which went down about three metres to this bubbling river that was saying to me, "Come here, Alex. I'm going to swallow you all up!" It was obvious that as soon as we got into the rafts we would fall straight out. But we didn't! We pulled our raft down the slope between some trees and our instructor, who was called Have Ear got us all to jump in. I jumped in first and got in the front. Then I said, "Laura, jump in over there," pointing at the other position at the front, which she did. I told her that Skip had told me that the front is the driest part of the raft and I was going to stay dry if I could help it. Skip was in the back with Leigh. Skip must've wanted to get really wet! Four more Scouts filled up the middle spaces, then Have Ear jumped in and straight away we were off! Have Ear had huge oars that stretched across the whole of the river and mine was so short that it didn't even reach the water. We spun around a bit and hit a few big waves, all the time holding on to a rope round the top of the raft with one hand. After the first wave I was really wet and Skip was wrong. I looked back and saw that Skip was laughing to Leigh and they were both completely dry, so he had made a bit of a mistake. Then Have Ear got into a bit of difficulty cos the raft turned round and Have Ear couldn't turn it back again and there was a really big wave coming and Have Ear shouted, "Get down!" but Have Ear didn't seem too worried and I got down and Laura screamed and the raft went down backwards first like it was diving into the wave and then Skip screamed! And then Have Ear shouted, "Positions!" and I sat back up and Skip and Leigh were soaked soaked! And who's in the dry spot now, Skip? cos Laura and I didn't get any water on us at all only a few drops. We were still wet through though. Then I looked back and saw that the three other rafts that were following us were all coming down backwards as well so maybe that's a difficult bit of the river for the instructors to deal with properly. Then we were allowed to jump in the river which Laura and I did so long as we stayed in the safety position which we also did. The river was running quite fast and we were allowed to swim against the tide - then Martin appeared. He had floated down from the raft behind but he wasn't swimming against the tide. He was on his back, but instead of crossing his arms across his chest and touching his shoulders like we had been taught to, he was patting his head with both hands and Skip and Leigh were patting their heads with one hand each and were laughing like children, which is what they probably are. They'll never be Chief Scout. Then Have Ear told us to get back in the raft which wasn't so easy but we managed it cos we are fit. Martin couldn't manage to get back into his raft cos he was still laughing and everyone on his boat was patting their heads with one hand and I just don't know what's so funny. Martin even did it again at dinner when we were having curry and all the leaders laughed again. I don't know what's wrong with them. I'll ask Nadia in the morning. She'll tell me.

Then Have Ear said that it was time for lunch. We paddled over to the bank and got out and scrambled up to where the coach was waiting with our lunch. We all had to be sterilised cos we had been in the river. We sat on the grass and had sandwiches and I had salami which is Italian and which I like, though normally on pizzas. In the morning we have to fill in a sheet of paper with our name and what filling we would like in our sandwich. It was okay yesterday cos we just had plain bread and so Nathan had a jam sandwich. Today Laura had jam cos otherwise she would have to have cheese all week or egg or marmite or just butter or nothing. What the ABC leaders didn't tell us though was that each day we had different bread and today we had sweary bread cos I asked Skip what it was called and it had olives and rosemary (which is a herb – not Laura's mum) which is fine with salami cos it's just like a cold pizza but not so good with strawberry jam so Laura didn't eat it apart from picking the olives off the top and then she just had a banana. Bananas come from Italy I think. Skip also said that the sweary bread has something called extra virgin olive oil drizzled over it, whatever that is. Well I know that olive oil comes from olives and they squash them or something but what's extra virgin? I'd no idea. I'ld have to ask. But I wasn't going to ask Graham. He probably wouldn't know anyway. I sat with Marculf and he was in a different raft and he had been sitting in the middle cos he said it was not so bumpy in the middle. It is also a good place to sit cos you don't get wet cos the people in front and behind act like a great big shield so I said to Laura that we should sit in the middle in the afternoon which we did.

On the way back to the raft I asked Nadia what virgin meant and she said that it was someone who hadn't been kissed. Then I asked her what extra virgin meant and she said that that was someone who hadn't had their hand held ever. This must be very sad. There can't be many virgins in England, especially not in Chislehurst. Maybe there are a few more in Italy cos that's where the virgins come from.

Laura and I made sure that we were the first back to our raft and we got in the middle and swapped with Shanice and Josh who got in the front and Skip and Leigh got in the back AGAIN! We went further down the river and it was getting faster and rougher cos we were getting nearer the sea. Have Ear said that we were going to get some more, "Get downs!" but we were prepared and we weren't going to get wet. Then Have Ear lost control again and we went down sideways and on my side and down a big wave and I got really really soaked and Laura got soaked as well and so did Leigh cos he was on my side but Skip was still fairly dry. Further on down the river we paddled past a great big pipe that stuck out into the river with loads of smelly stuff coming out of it. I asked Laura what she thought it was and she said, "Poo" so at least when we jumped in we were further up the river. Then Have Ear said we could jump in and some of the Scouts did but Laura and I didn't. Whilst we waited for the others Have Ear told us that we had just done a level two white water course. I'm glad we're not going to do a level three. Have Ear said that the courses go up to level six but as level six is impossible - if anyone ever manages it without dying then it becomes a level five so level two is enough for me for now, thank you very much. Have Ear is a nice man cos he looks very happy. He's always smiling like Laura. He then told Laura that she must be a happy girl cos she's always smiling. Then she said, "I wasn't smiling when my hamster died." Then Have Ear looked sad and said. "Oh, I am sorry. When did your 'amster die?" And Laura said, "Two hundred and eighty-four days ago," but she didn't cry but she wasn't smiling any more. Have Ear said, "Oh" and that was that.

When we got back to the coach Christoph said that we couldn't come on HIS coach cos we were all wet but we had nowhere to get changed so we had to keep our WET suits on. I don't know why he thought we would be getting on dry. Anyway it's not his coach but Planet said that it was fine cos we had a big roll of black sacks in the hold. We then had to take one black sack each, go up the coach steps one at a time, put our feet in the black sack and hop to a seat and turn round and sit on the black sack. This all took rather a long time but finally we were ready to go. Barnaby sat next to me and then said that he was desperate for a wee. Josh leant over his seat and said, "Just go in your black sack, cos it's waterproof unless you've made a hole in it and no one will know." I then had to inspect Barnaby's black sack and it looked okay but I said that just in case I would go up the front and get another one from Planet so that Barnaby could be doubled bagged like they do in the supermarket for alcoholics. I hopped up the aisle and got another sack from Planet cos I said that Barnaby may have sprung a leak and then Martin patted his head again and Planet laughed. I hopped back up to Barnaby and sat down. Then Barnaby had to stand up cos he couldn't get his second black sack on, and I had to sort of dress him like when mummies put little children's pants on. He jumped into the second sack and I pulled it up. Then he sat down again. Now he said that he couldn't wee even though he was bursting cos he was sitting down and he might do a poo so he had to stand up again. Then he said, "It's fine, I'm weeing," but he said it quite quietly and then after about ten minutes he said, "I've finished" and sat down and there was no leak. A few minutes later I was talking to Torchy across the aisle when Laura started screaming, "Barnaby's on fire! Barnaby's on fire!" Graham came hopping up the aisle and Torchy told him it was fine and that Barnaby was just having a wee. I turned round and Barnaby was on fire but Torchy said calmly, "It's okay, it's just a bit, well rather a lot. But all the same it's just steam." Well then everyone wanted a go and so all the boys and Laura (cos the other girls didn't take part or else they did but they stayed sitting down cos that's what they're used to) all stood up and soon the coach was full of steam like we were in a sauna and Torchy was patting his head like he was doing a drum roll and we all laughed, although I don't know why, and then we weed some more and Christoph had to put the windscreen wipers on.

When we arrived back at the campsite we all stood up and then I realised that we were all standing in big pools of wee and so we had to hop down the coach like we were babies splashing about in paddling pools with a couple of centimetres of water in them. Then we had to get down the steps which was a bit of a challenge, then we could step out of the black sacks and empty the contents onto the grass verge. When we got back to the storage area we took off our wetsuits and then they had to be disinfected in a big barrel, then rinsed, then hung up to dry. Josh didn't take his wet suit off with the rest of us. He walked off to the showers with it still on. Joe told me later that he had got the wrong idea completely of going to the toilet in a wetsuit and had done a number two.

Once we had all showered (Josh twice) and dried off and got changed we were supposed to go on a trip to an authentic Italian village but ended up at Car Four which is a huge hypermarket. Barnaby said that these huge shops are called spacemarkets. On the coach Martin stood up and announced that the camp bank would be open for shopping at the side of the coach. Once in the car park Martin opened the camp bank and I took out ten Euros. Josh just stood there looking sad so I asked him what the matter was. He said that there was nothing worth buying at the side of the coach. I had to explain to him that we weren't shopping at the side of the coach, we were getting our money out at the side of the coach to go shopping. However, there was nothing that I really wanted to buy either so I just wandered round looking. In the end I bought some runny cheese to take home to mummy cos she likes runny cheese. I also bought her a postcard and a stamp and the same for Chloe cos she couldn't come on the France Italy trip but she didn't say why. When we all met back up outside the coach we looked at what everyone had bought. Aaron had bought a parcel tape dispenser. Joe had bought some after shave and a wok. Everyone else had bought food. Jake had bought some Grenadine sirop. Barnaby and Josh were last to appear. They came walking back to the coach looking very sheepish. Barnaby said that they had been playing volleyball. I can't see why that should be a problem. Then he said that they had been using a packet of chocolate brioche as the ball and the shelves as a net (that you couldn't see over) then they got told off so had to stop. Barnaby said that he had bought some violent sirop which was a purple colour. He said that sirop is a bit like orange squash only more concentrated and you have to mix it with loads of water and it's not spelt properly like it should be syrop I think. As for Aaron and his parcel tape dispenser, I asked him why he bought it. "Cos I don't have one," was his stupid answer. I don't have a Chieftain tank, but I'm not going to go and buy one, not that they sell them in Car Four. It felt like the patrol station all over again.

We had salmon tonight which is a fish. Bendy does the cooking and she said that she cooks salmon in the dishwasher cos it steams the fish really well and she doesn't have a poacher. Mummy does eggs in a poacher and there's no way a whole salmon can fit in a poacher even if she had one cos a whole salmon to feed all of us must be enormous like a whale but I didn't say anything and she gets whole salmon in the local market. Barnaby came and sat down in the messy tent and was very wet and with sticky out hair. He had been playing football on the pitch cos we were allowed to on Monday evenings, so that means once, and the sprinklers came on. He then decided that this would be a quick way to get his hair washed while playing football so he went and got a handful of shampoo and rubbed it in his hair, but by the time that he arrived back at the football pitch the sprinklers had gone off and it was too late to go for another shower so now he had half-washed hair and no water. He told Skip that he would go and shower after dinner but actually he just stuck his head under the tap in the toilets.

After dinner I took a deep breath and told Skip quietly that he was not to fancy Clair as she is married and so is he. He just gave me a funny look and said that it was okay and that I didn't need to tell Hugo's mum, which also sounded very suspicious. I can't really tell Hugo cos I don't want to get him involved and I can't phone her cos no one's allowed their phones on camp. Fortunately I bought a postcard to send mummy. I'll have to send one to Hugo's mummy instead. It should get there without a postcode.

Tonight was quiz night and it was leaders' teams v. Scouts' teams. I was in my tent team, me, Marculf, Joe and Nathan. We didn't do very well. Marculf was hopeless. We played our joker on music cos Marculf insisted he knew everything there was to know. We scored nought. Then Marculf said that he thought it was a round on breakfast cereals like CocoPops and stuff. I think he thought that the round was on muesli. I'm not sure how you can ask a round of questions of muesli. Hopefully Marculf isn't either otherwise he's odder that I thought. When Glug asked which singer has had a hit single in each of five decades Marculf said Madonna which was stupid as when she was alive there were no singles. No music either probably. The answer was Cliff Richard who no one's heard of. I think he was in the

Rolling Stones.

**Alex**

At breakfast today Planet announced that it was going to be
a very hot day and that we must all make especially sure that
we all start the day with loads of sun cream on and that after
breakfast we must go and get our tubes and jars. We lined
up for inspection and Planet gave us an extra bit of his
special what he called Factor 100 cream to go on top of our
normal sun cream. It was a bit odd that it was in a yoghurt
pot but I didn't say anything. Maybe he makes his own
cream, like daddy and his mosquito oil.

After breakfast while we were being sun creamed there was
a bit of a commotion in the sick tent and Graham went to
see what was going on with yours truly following behind.
Graham had to roll up the tent front in case he was a speedo
but this meant that everyone could see what was going on.
And we were all watching. Nathan was out of bed and he
was covered in orange and purple, like someone had been
painting him with a very big paint brush. Jake and Barnaby
were just standing in the tent with orange and purple
dripping from their mouths. "What the sweary sweary
sweary sweary have you two been up to?" Graham asked
them. Jake was the first to speak. "Nothing, Graham." "Then
what sweary sweary sweary sweary sweary have you been
eating or drinking?" Well, of course, after that sort of
interrogation they weren't going to say sirop of Grenadine
and Violent sirop mixed together and not watered down for
breakfast on top of bacon and eggs were they shots? But
Laura did. "You've been drinking sweary sweary sirop
shots?" Graham screamed at them, "Why?" "Well dad does

it." "He doesn't do it with dodgy French sweary sweary sirops does he? He does it with normal drinks like Alabama Slammers or Pink Pussies. How much have you drunk?" "A litre each, mixed together." "And what are you doing being sick over Nathan?" "Well," said Barnaby, "You said it was the sick tent." "IT'S THE TENT THAT YOU GO IN IF I MEAN WHEN YOU'VE **BEEN** SICK YOU SWEARY SWEARY TWAT NOT TO GO IN **TO BE** SICK." In the quiet space that followed Nathan looked up, then down and then said quietly to the floor, "And I was just beginning to feel a little bit better."

It seems that we aren't the only camp to have sick issues as we were supposed to be going off to France today to go canoeing down a big river but there is sickness in the other camp and there is quite a bit of sickness in this camp so we're staying where we are. We wondered what we were going to go when we weren't supposed to be here. No one seemed to know what to do so we decided to have a game of Scout volleyball but not in a hypomarket. We went and got our camping mats that weren't being used and were just in the way. Aaron lent us his parcel tape dispenser telling us, "I knew it would come in useful." We taped the ends of the four camping mats to the top of the volleyball net so that they hung down and made a sort of curtain, one that couldn't be opened and closed. The idea was that we played volleyball as usual but couldn't see the ball until it was coming over the net. We were just about to start when Graham shouted, "Scouts!" We gathered round and he told us that we were going to go and do some kayaking and subs. We knew what to do to get ready - bouncy aids, helmets, paddles but no wet suits as we were going to go on a lake that was owned by a golf course. Golf people are rich so I thought they probably had a heated lake so it would be nice and warm. We got on the coach but this time we had to take towels and a change of clothes otherwise we would have had to have walked home. We got to the lake and Bendy and Bagpuss were in charge. We were put into two big groups and one group did kayaks and the other group did subs. Then we had a packed lunch and then we swapped over.

We had something called a panini which was flat and hard a bit like a stale sandwich. Sometimes mummy does me a sandwich made with bread that is stale, once it even had green bits on it but then I put it in the sandwich toaster for a couple of minutes to cook it and it was yummy. Except for when mummy didn't have any sandwich filling so I just used what was in the fridge and so had a fish finger, apricot jam and custard toastie. This wasn't quite so yummy. Laura said that paninis were supposed to be a bit hard cos they're like ironed when you buy them in the cafe but these weren't ironed they were just cold and hard. Yuck. No one liked them. I threw mine in the lake when no one was watching but it floated. Then it disappeared, probably cos there's a crocodile or something in the lake.

I had done kayaks before but subs were new. They're like body boards only you stand up on them and paddle standing up. It's really hard work. Kayaks were fun. Bendy made us stand on them, jump on them, chase each other in them and at one point we had to try and touch the very front of our kayak with our nose. It's almost impossible but it didn't matter cos the heaters were turned to high and so the water was really warm. I got back on my kayak / sub quickly though just in case the croc. was still hungry or didn't like panini either. It's been a very sunny day, again.

Once we were all worn out, it was time to get changed and go back to camp. We got changed outside beside the lake and the girls had to go up the far end behind some bushes and the boys went and got changed behind the pile of kayaks. All the Italian golfers who were sitting outside the clubhouse were just staring at us (not when we were getting changed cos we were hiding but when we were kayaking and talking). I hoped that they knew that we were going to be going on their lake cos they would have been quite cross if we had just turned up and jumped in.

While I was waiting for everyone to get ready Laura came over and said, "Follow me!" in a whisper and she walked past without looking at me and Aaron. I followed her into the nice cool clubhouse with Aaron following behind where she told me that she hadn't bothered getting changed cos she was going to have to have a shower when we got back to camp so she just put her clothes on top of her swimming costume. "The thing is," she said, "they're nearly dry already so Christoph won't say anything. Come on, quick, we've got a few minutes. Let's have a look round." We walked along a big corridor with photos of lots of important people and into a bar area. There was a lady behind the bar who smiled at us. "Come on," said Laura, "I've got five Euros." We walked up to the bar. "Cosa vorresti?" she said. Aaron whispered to us that she wanted to know what we wanted to drink. Before I could say, "Three Cokes please" cos that's what we never get at camp, Aaron asked, "Do you have a pink pussy?" The lady looked at us a bit strange so I said, "Three Cokes." "Ah, yes," she said and went off and poured three large Cokes with ice and lemon and a big bowl of somethings and said with her fingers in the air like TEN Euros and I had no

Euros and Aaron had no Euros and Laura had just five. Then a man appeared and said something to the lady and gave her ten Euros. Then he said to us, "You've given my friends and me a good giggle. Where are you from and I said, "Chislehurst, it's in England." And the man said, "Yes, I know. That's where the caves are," which is true. And then he said that he was English and was living in Italy then he said something to the lady and she screamed like with laughing and then Skip appeared and said that he had been looking for us and we had better get on the coach before Graham sees us which we did and we were allowed to take our drinks even though they were in posh glasses and the nibbley somethings with us and we got on the coach and then Skip went and told Graham that we were on the coach already.

On the way back to camp Bagpuss came down the aisle and helped himself to our bowl of nibbleys and he said they were called Frecco and they're a sort of crisp and they were yummy and we never told Graham cos he would wonder how we got them. Bagpuss said that the bar that we were in was for members only so we were lucky to get served and then I told Bagpuss what Aaron had said to the lady and Bagpuss laughed and patted his head and now I'm fed up with leaders laughing at me and patting their heads so this evening I got Barnaby to text his mummy and ask her what it means if a leader pats his head.

When we got back to the campsite we went in the messy tent for a drink and there was a big box in there which said Mr John Hemming-Clark, c/o ABC Adventure Travel and the address. Skip looked at it and took it into his tent. I wonder what it is?

At dinner Clair told us that we all looked very well, with our nice tans. Apart from Graham who had gone very red from being in the sun too much. Planet smiled and said that you would think that the parents would know how to look after themselves, wouldn't you? But they obviously don't. And Planet was up to no good. After dinner, whilst we were washing up, Planet came over and told me what he had been up to. Whilst we were out yesterday he had gone into Graham's tent and found his Clarains Instant Smooth Self-Tanning jar and scooped all of it out and put it in a yoghurt pot. He then squirted shaving cream into Graham's empty jar. I don't think shaving cream has any protection against the sun, so no wonder Graham has gone red. "So now he not only sees red but he is red!" and we both laughed so I patted my head and Planet laughed some more.

After dinner we were told that we were going to have a go at fencing. Marculf went up to Planet, who had made the announcement, to complain. He said, "As far as I'm concerned we are on an activity holiday, not a gardening holiday. Anyway, Skip can teach us how to do fencing." Planet then had to explain to Marculf that fencing was a sport from the old days. "It's a bit like stabbing someone, but you get points." "You get points for hurting someone?" "No, you can't hurt them. You wear special clothes and you get points for touching various parts of the body." "So, if I poke Barnaby's eyes out do I get loads of points?" "No, you get told off." Then Marculf went and told Barnaby that he should watch out cos he's going to stab him in the eyes and get maximum points. Barnaby then said that if Marculf got him in the eyes then Barnaby would stab Marculf to death. Marculf then told him that that would be quite difficult, "if you can't see me." There the conversation ended cos pudding was ready. Laura had three puddings cos she likes chocolate and then we played catch with a packet of Haribos. You have to throw each one in the air and count as high as you can from one before catching it in your mouth. Each time you catch one you get another go. Laura caught thirty-seven cos she was counting the number of Haribos as well. I hope she's not sick.

After dinner we all had to put on thick clothes like you would use for a padded tent and we leant how to jump, "hon guard" and how to stab someone for maximum points, (not in the eyes). Night Rate told me that Planet was the World Champion at fencing which was quite cool. I wonder if he's ever poked anyone's eyes out? I bet he has if he's got maximum points.

I decided that I wouldn't tell Skip again that he's not to fancy another woman but as I can't tell him I've written a postcard to Hugo's mummy. We were all given a postcard today with a stamp on it and we were supposed to write something to our own mummies and daddies but I decided that I must use my postcard for something more important. I wrote, "Hi. It has come to my notice that Skip may be misbehaving with Clair. It's none of my business but I think you should know. From Anonymous." I had put, "From Alex" but that would be rather silly so I crossed it off. I don't know Hugo's post code and I don't want to ask him so I left it off, but I've put, "UK" at the end so it should get there. I'll post it in the morning. I've also sent one to Chloe saying that we're having a great time and hope that she's okay.

**Tuesday 11th August**

**Skip**

We came back from kayaking and SUPBs which is a new thing for me, they're Stand Up Paddle Boards, to find a large box waiting for me with a French post mark. I've brought it into my tent and opened it and it's no less than a case of Scotch whisky! I know that the manager of the petrol station was going to send me a thank-you letter but I didn't know that it was going to accompany twelve bottles of single-malt. Fantastic! There's almost one each for every leader (Scout and ABC) so long as Graham isn't considered a leader. I know what the Scouts think!

**Tuesday 11th August**
**Skip**
**Late**

Once the Scouts had gone to bed I told the leaders what was in the parcel to accompany the thank you letter that had been sent thanking me for saving the petrol station although, as I pointed out to the team, the fact of the matter was that I didn't have much to do with the rescue. To which Graham said, "No, and had you been looking after the Scouts properly the fire wouldn't have happened. And then for you to be sent a case of whisky when you are partially responsible for the fire in the first place is a bit stupid." So Graham is now definitely not a leader in any capacity and I shall enjoy handing out the bottles tomorrow in front of him. Mind you, given that I may get "the scowl" maybe I'll just leave it for now.

**Wed 12th August**
**Alex**

At breakfast Skip asked us all to give him our postcards so that he could post them. This was going to mean trouble! I thought that Skip wouldn't notice if I didn't give him mine so I didn't say anything but then he counted them and there was one missing so I told him that it was me and that I had lost it. As I was being told off Marculf appeared and said, "Here it is!" and was waving my postcard in the air. He said, "I saw you put it under your pillow." He went to give it to Skip but I managed to grab it. I told Skip that I had written a very private note to mummy and that he wasn't to read it. Then he said I could put it in an envelope so Planet went and got one. Then when he got back I put my postcard in the envelope and then Skip told me to write my address on it. Well, that wasn't going to work so I said that I couldn't remember it. Phew! But then Martin said that he had all the Scouts' home addresses and so he looked it up and wrote it on the envelope. Then I asked if I could post it but Skip said, "No" so now mummy was going to get a card written by me ('cos she knows my handwriting) telling her about Skip and Clair. I was going to be in so much trouble. Martin gave the pile of post cards to Planet with my envelope on top and Planet wandered off. Then I realised that I had another one for Chloe so I could have swapped but I'll just have to find a post box myself for that one.

Today we were told that we were going to visit a ski resort and go swimming so everyone had to go and pack a rucksack and put loads of sun cream on again though I didn't think it was going to be very sunny if it was snowing in the mountains. I quickly packed a hat and a woolly. Whilst everyone was getting ready I went to the office and went in cos there was no one around and found the pile of postcards with my envelope on top so I did something very naughty and I took it and put it in my pocket. Then Planet came into the office so I had to tell him that I was sorry and that I had stolen my envelope. He just laughed and said, "Whatever" then said that I couldn't really steal my own envelope once it had been given to me as it was then mine so that was okay. Anyway, whilst I was in there I saw on the wall a big notice that had on it, "WiFi Code" so there is one and I'm going to be rich!

We got on the coach and Graham stood at the front of the coach and said that we were going to a place called "Pillar" which was just up the road. We drove into a car park and we saw loads of little cable cars on a cable going up the mountain. Barnaby said that they were called "gondolas" which I knew wasn't true cos that's what they call the long boats on the canals in Venice. I didn't say anything though. We then had to wait outside the coach while Skip and Clair went to buy some tickets. Whilst we were waiting I saw that outside one of the shops there was a post box! So I got my envelope out and opened it and took out the post card and put it in the post box and put the envelope in my pocket. And nobody saw. And I posted the one for Chloe as well. Success!

We were given a ticket each and told to look after it otherwise we would have to walk back down the mountain. We then had to wave our ticket in front of a barrier thing and then the gate opened. (I think there was a man watching to make sure that we had a ticket otherwise he wouldn't have let the gate open. I don't know how he knows that the ticket is in date though as we were able to keep the ticket when we got back down.) Laura said that when she goes skiing she puts her ticket in a pocket in her arm and she just waves her arm at the barrier and it opens. This is obviously stupid cos the man can't see whether you have a ticket or not. I don't think Laura's been skiing.

We had eight Scouts in each little cable car and we had to sit
down. I went in the first little cable car and it left the
getting-on building and then we went up the wire. It got
really high up really quickly and Laura said that she was
going to be sick so I said to her to go out of the window. She
said that she couldn't reach and I said that she would have
to stand up and she said she wasn't allowed to and I said
that it was an emergency. Then Barnaby showed me a sign
which showed a hand holding some rubbish and a red cross
across it. I then told him it was an emergency and, "You
won't want Laura being sick over you, will you." So he said,
"Okay," and Laura stood up and the little cable car swayed
and I told Laura not to hold the door cos it would open and
she would fall out. Then Barnaby said that he wondered if it
was okay if Scouts were allowed to fall out of the gondola. I
can't see that it really matters cos they would be dead
anyway unless there was loads of snow to land on which
there wasn't today, just grass and roads and buildings and
why weren't there any seat belts?

Laura grabbed a pole above the window and leant out and
was really really sick and we all looked down and the sick all
separated and below us from a big stream to like hailstones
about a thousand feet below was a party in a big house with
a huge garden and a big swimming pool and it was like
Laura was shooting at the people in the pool with her
Haribos dive-bombing the people in the pool and there were
more than thirty-seven pieces so it wasn't just the Haribos it
was the chocolate and breakfast as well. Then the people
looked up at us and were pointing so Laura sat down again
and we giggled and Laura said that she felt much better

then.

We went up and up and up and every time we went over a pylon the little cable car swung and I felt quite sick but I wasn't and everyone was really quiet. Eventually we arrived at the top building and I didn't know how to open the door but all of a sudden it opened itself – a bit like the gates at the bottom. I'm glad that the doors didn't do that whilst we were half way up the lift otherwise Laura might have fallen out and ended up in the swimming pool along with her sick. I don't think she would have survived though maybe she would've cos there's that man, Professor Splash, who's dived into a couple of centimetres of water from thousands of feet up so it can be done. I don't know if Professor Laura could do it though. Not if she's just been sick.

Anyway, the spooky doors opened and we jumped out and then a man appeared and told us to wait. Then Skip arrived with Planet and Aaron and some others and the man was jabbering on in Italian and I had no idea what was being said but eventually Skip and Planet just said "Sorry" and we were allowed to leave the building. Aaron said that the man was complaining about something but he didn't know what and Skip didn't say anything.

When we got out of the building it was like we were in another world. There was no snow but lots of people wandering around with no woollies on cos it was very hot. There was a hotel with a swimming pool but we weren't allowed to go in it cos there was no life guard and there was a long zip wire but we couldn't go on it cos Skip said that it hadn't been wrist-assessed so we decided to walk up the slope a bit to where there were ice creams being sold.

Barnaby said to Skip that we weren't allowed to have an ice-cream up there cos they hadn't been wrist-assessed either but Skip took no notice.

We sat down in the shade to eat our packed lunch and whilst we were eating it I saw some foreign Scouts. I knew that they were Scouts cos they were wearing Scout scarves. I suppose they could have been Muslims but they would have been black scarves and they put them on their heads, even the men. But these were Scouts. So I went over to them with Nathan cos he had finished his lunch (no surprise) and we asked them where they had come from. They were looking at a large map and they said, "Aosta" which is the town that we got the little cable car from. I said that we came up on the little cable car and asked them if they did the same. They said that they had walked. I didn't believe them cos it took us twenty minutes in the little cable car but they showed us the path on their map that was going higgledy-piggledy up the mountain under the little cable car and it had taken them all morning. Nathan then asked them if they had been sicked on but I don't think that they understood, fortunately. Then I asked them where they lived in Aosta but they said that they didn't live there – they lived in Pizza which is where pizzas come from. Then Skip came over and when they told him that they came from Pizza he stood up straight with his arms by his side like he was at alert then he leant over and asked, "Is this how you stand on parade?" which I thought was a bit rude but they all laughed so that was okay. But I don't know why it's so funny. I thought that I might pat my head but I didn't. Then I said "goodbye" and they said "chow" which is a sort of dog. I thought that they must be barking. Ha, ha.

After lunch Skip announced that we could go swimming at a local pool once our food had gone down.

Oh my goodness. Laura went as white as a sheet.

"It's not too near here, is it, Skip" she asked. No it wasn't, thank goodness. Can you imagine if we had to swim in Laura's sick? Still, I suppose the Haribos would have been washed and sterilised with the chorine so it would probably have been okay. We had to go back down in the little cable car. So it wasn't just our dinner going down it was us as well. I waved my card at the barrier and said, "Hey, presto!" and the barrier opened. Naturally, as I am a born leader, everyone followed me and said, "Hey, presto!" like we were the Magic Circle. Then we got in the little cable cars. I sat with Laura again but we had Skip and Martin with us now. I asked her if she felt sick. She said that she didn't but that if she was then she was going to be sick inside the little cable car and not outside it. When we got to where Laura had been sick on the way up I looked out of the window. There were even more people at the house below but there was no one in the pool. Maybe they were waiting for their dinner to go down as well.

Barnaby asked Skip if we could do some "Apres Ski." Skip said we couldn't cos we hadn't done any skiing which was a bit unfair cos there was no snow and if there was snow we would've. Then Barnaby asked if we could do some Apres No Ski" and Skip said something to Martin and they both laughed.

Soon we were back down on dry land and back on the coach and on our way to a swimming pool that did have a lifeguard. The pool isn't far from where we're staying. It's on the other side of the river hidden behind a high wall with quite a drop down one side to the river. The pool was full of Italian families and after a short while it got a bit boring. Apart from when Nathan jumped in at the deep end and Laura said that she thought someone had turned on the wave machine. Then Barnaby found a ball in the pool and we started playing with it. That is, until this man jumped in the pool and just took it from Barnaby. But instead of playing with it he got out of the pool and went and sat in his deckchair with the ball beside him. Laura then went over and asked the man if we could play with the ball please and he said, "No." Then she said to him, "Weren't you a child once?" and then she started to cry and he still said no. What a meanie! However, soon after that the man fell asleep so Barnaby just went over and took it. When the man woke up and saw Barnaby with the ball on the other side of the pool he shouted, "Give me back my ball!" cos he was English, or spoke English at least. Well, I suppose he could have been Austrian or something and be saying, "Hallo. Isn't it a lovely day?" in Austrian but which sounded like, "Give me back my ball!" Barnaby kicked the ball over the pool but it bounced before Mr Angry could catch it and bounced over the wall. Barnaby ran round the pool and clambered up the wall. The ball was nowhere to be seen. All there was was a car park and the white water rafting river crashing and bashing down the valley. Oh dear! It was time to go. We got changed but as we were all wet still we walked back - over the bridge and down the other side of the river and down the footpath to our camp. We had only gone a few metres when I saw the ball in the river! It had got stuck on some rocks and as Skip and the other leaders were in front and not looking, Barnaby clambered down to the ball and recovered it. Tee, hee!

One-nil to the Scouts. When we got back to camp, as it was such a bouncy ball it was great to play volleyball with. We were in the middle of a very bouncy game when Mr Angry appeared. We thought that he had followed us down the road but actually he was living on the same campsite only in the bit with wine. He shouted at us, "Give me back my ball!" and Skip said, "Would you mind leaving this area please otherwise I shall get a member of staff?" Then Barnaby shouted at Mr Angry, "You can have your ball back when you've done some washing-up!" which sounded like just the sort of thing that Skip would say so we all laughed and Mr Angry wandered off. Barnaby did give it back later. He kicked it back. He kicked it back into Mr Angry's camping area whilst they were having dinner. Judging by the "crash" that followed I think Mr Angry will not only have needed a washing-up cloth tonight but also a large dustpan and brush, and a very big mop, and an enormous sorry to all his friends.

Dinner was fine. It was stellette pasta which I had never eaten before. It was star shaped and I must have eaten thousands. Goodness knows how long it takes to cut all the little shapes out. It takes me half an hour just to cut six cookies for cooking so it would take me years just to cut out my dinner. Lasagne must be much quicker cos it's just the sheets.

I scoffed my meal and went out to the toilet via my tent where I got some paper and a pen. The office was locked so I went round the back and peered through the sluts in the window. The light was on and I could read the WiFi password on the wall opposite so I wrote it down quickly and stuffed it in my pocket.

Later on Martin came and sat down with Torchy and they brought out a big box of power cord. They've taken all the wire out though cos that's probably quite expensive so we're just left with the covering and some white strands inside. They have all sorts of colours. Martin asked us what we would like to make. I had no idea what you could make with it so I just let them decide. Martin said that wobbles were good and soon he had some of us trying to make them. It's not easy! Torchy had some power cord that was whitish but when he took it outside and shone his laser torch on it it glowed green. It was fab. That's what I wanted my wobble made out of. I tried it on and I loved it and I kept it on all evening. Torchy charged it up so that it was glowing like a glow worm, or whatever.

While we were busy with our power cord knitting or whatever it's called, Planet appeared and asked if Martin could make bigger wobbles that were a bit narrower. Of course Martin could, he's an expert. Planet then explained that he wanted a power cord bracelet for his ankle. "Don't you think you have enough?" Martin asked him but Planet obviously thought that he hadn't so he set to work making Planet a luminous ankle bracelet like my wobble. However, ankle bracelets don't slide on and off feet like wobbles do scarves so Planet had to have his ankle bracelet welded round his ankle so that the only way that he could take it off would be to cut it. Torchy charged it up and we turned off the lights in the messy tent. It looked very cool. Planet seemed very happy and said that all the ABC staff would be wanting them. All this wobble making took forever and it was getting late and there weren't many of us left so Martin sent me off to bed. How was I to know that Nathan was still

266

half-awake inside our tent? I walked quietly over to our tent and carefully unzipped the flap and tiptoed in. Then Nathan screamed like he wanted to wake the whole campsite up. "What's the matter. Nathan?" I asked him. "It's only me, Alex." "I thought you were a ghost," he said. "All I could see was a green luminous thing floating towards me." "Oh, grow up, Nathan" I said to him. "There's no such thing as ghosts. I thought you said you were a mature Scout. Mature people don't scream like that." With that I heard a real scream – louder than Nathan's – coming from the direction of the ABC Leaders' camp.

Planet had obviously just gone to bed as well.

**Thursday 13th August**
**Alex**
**Breakfast**
I've sold the WiFi password to Barnaby for twenty Euros and now he's busy selling it to all the Scouts (even those that don't have phones 'cos they don't want to miss out) for five Euros each, not that he needs the money.

We have just been informed that due to extra time in Italy we can go white water rafting and we're going to do level three which I'm not ready for so if I die and I write no more in my diary, I love you mummy and please look after Scottie Dog. He's in my rucksack (at the bottom so no one can see him).

**Thursday 13th August**
**Alex**
**Evening**
I'm alive! But only just. Level three was fun though. We

went up the valley this time where the river was running even quicker. We pulled off the main road and went down a track to where Have Ear and the others were waiting with our rafts. Have Ear looked worried. We carried our rafts to the edge of the river. We had the same teams again. Have Ear said that this time we had to get into the boat all together and then "Get down!" straightaway. I did as I was told and, in fact, didn't "Get Up!" again until the end of the rapids. I still got wet though and we all had to get changed before Christoph would let us back on the coach. It was a bit like levels one and two only more bouncy and we couldn't jump in the river.

We had a bit of free time before dinner. Laura came to my tent (round the back) and said that the WiFi password didn't work. I told her that she probably had to be near the office building cos that was where the flashing box thingy was and off she went.

Dinner was called and half the Scouts were missing. Graham went off to find them and I knew that if he found them they would get into trouble so I told Skip where they probably were and off he went. Soon they were all back in the messy tent and dinner started. Then Graham appeared and announced that he had looked everywhere and couldn't find any of them and Skip said, "They're here!" Then Graham looked really cross and said, "Where were they?" and Skip said, "Washing their hands in the toilets" and Graham said, "Oh" and sat down to two portions of chocolate placenta cos we had eaten all the mains.

After dinner Glug appeared in the messy tent with a huge wooden ashtray thing with spouts and a lid on top. He told the leaders that it was called "une coupe de l'amitie" which means a friendly coffee. So I don't know what an unfriendly coffee is. Probably the sort that you have by yourself with no one to talk to. Skip wanted to know what was in it cos it was steaming and Glug said, "Coffee and stuff." "Stuff" probably means sugar and milk and cream and March mallows and things like that. He told the leaders that they have spout each and once someone picks it up it had to be passed round and not put down until all the coffee has been drunk.

Now we had the highlight of the day! Skip read a chapter of his book, "In You Go! A year or two in the life of a Scout leader!" He told us that it was a best-seller but that it wasn't suitable for Scouts to read, probably cos it had in it things like blood and words we wouldn't understand. He then said that he would read a bit that was okay so we all sat round him as he read a story about when some of the older Scouts made a giant pyramid catapult on an international camp and how they bombed some Guides with mini water-bombs, but halfway through Skip suddenly stopped reading mid sentence, then giggled and said that he couldn't read part of the chapter aloud and he missed a whole chunk out and the leaders then giggled. It was probably a word that we wouldn't understand or someone was injured and there was blood. When he had finished and everyone clapped, Martin said, "Your book is like une coupe de l'amitie... Once you've picked it up you can't put it down until it's finished!" and the leaders laughed and took another sip out of their ashtray. Then Graham added, "Yeah, they're both full of sh*t!" and no one laughed, apart from the Scouts and only then only cos Graham had said a sweary word.

Laura disappeared and came back a few minutes later and

sat next to me. She said that she had been round the back of the office with the others and whilst they had all been finishing off their texting and Facebook and whatever she had downloaded Skip's book and had found the bit he had been reading. I asked her if it had blood in it and she said, "No." I then asked her if it had a word in it that we wouldn't understand. "Far worse than that," she said. "I can't even say it. It looks a bit like 'proper elastic.'"^ Seeing as the chapter was all about a huge catapult it was probably some technical term so probably the problem was that Skip couldn't pronounce it either.

^*Prophylactic*

Whilst we were having hot choc. Bagpuss appeared with a very sweet, purple fluffy bear. "This is my little friend," he told us, "and she goes everywhere with me." I asked Bagpuss how he knew it was a she and he said he hoped she was cos she's called Amanda which I thought was a stupid name for a bear. "It's a panda," he explained. I then felt that the time was right to go and get Scottie Dog who had been sitting at the bottom of my rucksack for far too long. "What's that?!" said Nathan when Scottie Dog made his appearance but I didn't need to answer cos then most of the Scouts went and found their own little friends. Even Skip has an orange cat called Larry. Then the other leaders went off and got their little friends too. Except Graham. He has no friends. No friendly coffees for him then.

**Friday 14th August**
**Alex**
This morning we tried to go gorge scrambling again. We got all our gear together and jumped on the coach and went somewhere up the valley. We had to walk for miles until we

got to this huge waterfall but then it started to rain and thunder so we weren't allowed to go gorge scrambling again so we had to come back to get changed and pack and leave. However, it was raining so much that there was no point getting changed but Christoph wouldn't let us back on the coach so we had to all climb into the hold underneath the coach where the luggage goes and hold on to not much. It was a bit dark and very bumpy but great fun. Probably more fun than gorge not-scrambling. When we got back to camp we could hear Glug asking where we all were and then Christoph let us out of the hold and Barnaby said that we had been playing asylum seekers and we all laughed but the leaders didn't.

After lunch it was time to get on the coach (and not under it like this morning) for our long trip back to home. I am so tired. It's been a great holiday but we are now going to have to do the whole outward trip in reverse so I'm going to put down my pen and my diary and go to sleep.

**Saturday 15th August**
**Skip**
We're back home after our fabulous adventure. The only downside was when Nathan's mum picked him up and I had to tell her that he had been sick a couple of times. Then she said, "I think I know why. I was trying to get him to pack himself and he packed the wrong toothbrush." "And which one did he pack?" "The one that I normally use for cleaning round the rim of the upstairs toilet." And with that, Nathan was sick again.

**Saturday 15th August**
**Alex**

It's quite funny really. We've been on an adventure holiday but the best adventures we had weren't when we were doing our adventures but when we weren't. Still, I suppose that if we hadn't gone on an adventure holiday we wouldn't have had any adventures at all. And I know what I would rather have.

## Sunday 16th August
**Alex**

I am so much trouble. Mummy has unpacked my rucksack and is busy washing my dirty, smelly and wet stuff. She's found some pants that I didn't wear and I told her that Chief Scouts and people like James and Bear don't wear new pants every day, just clean ones and mummy looked a bit puzzled so I explained that Tegan had told me that her dad who is Gunner told her that he used to wear the same pants every day for four days and that after day one he would turn them round and that would do for day two then on day three he would turn them inside out and then on day four he would turn them round again. (Not that Gunner's going to be Chief Scout). Then mummy said, "Yeah and on day five he has to wash his trousers cos he's put sweary all over them," and then she laughed. So I told her that on days three and four he could wear his pants on the outside of his trousers and then mummy said, "Yeah and then he would have to wash the sofa and the car seat and his bicycle seat and anything else he sat on." This is a bit unfair cos he may not sit down for two days. Anyway, I've saved mummy having to do so much washing so I don't know why she's complaining.

Joe is in so much trouble. He texted me to tell me that his mummy couldn't find any of his pants when she was doing the washing yesterday and when she asked him where his pants were he said that he was wearing them and when she asked him what about the ones that he's not wearing he said that he was wearing all of them. She then looked at him a bit odd and said why? And Joe said that because she had told him to wear a new pair every day and she said, "Yes, but you're supposed to take the dirty ones off each time you sweary stupid boy." And there was me thinking that Joe hadn't been doing any poos all week cos he did look a bit bloated. Anyway then she made him take all his pants off there and then and after she had taken off Tuesday's she found a Panini and she was very cross. I can't think why, at least it would've warmed up after five days.

Barnaby will be in so much trouble as well. His hiking boots were so wet and muddy that his mummy told him that he would have to clean them so he put them in the microwave to dry them off so that he could scrape the mud off. He only gave them a minute so that they didn't catch fire and so no fire extinguishers would be needed but when he took them out of the microwave the soles had melted. He hasn't told his mummy yet though. I'm not sure when he will but he'll have to some time.

Chloe sent me a text to say that she had got my postcard but she said nothing else.

## Monday 31st August
**Alex**

Hallo diary. I am now back! That was a big gap! We went on holiday - me, Matthew, mummy and daddy. We went to Croatia but it wasn't as fun as Italy France so I didn't bother writing my diary. We stayed in someone's house that daddy knew which was lovely. It was a place called Milna and it has four bakeries cos people in Croatia like bread. I used to go out and buy the bread in the mornings cos mummy used to sleep a lot and daddy doesn't go shopping and Matthew was reading. It was really safe cos it was a little village in a marina and not many cars. I used to go into the furthest bakery and it was seven hundred and twenty-seven steps and it was great cos mummy used to leave out loads of kuna which is the Croatian currency. First I used to go to the ice cream man. His name is Toma like you're saying tomato quickly. He was half way to the bakery that was furthest away and I would have an ice cream that was called energy ice cream cos I needed one of those and it was in English. I had it with extra whipped cream. Then I would eat it and by the time I got to the furthest bakery I had finished it and I was really awake.

In the bakery they have French food like cross aunts and they have stuff in them like marmalade and custard so I would always buy an extra one and eat it on the way back to Toma. The lady's name in the bakery was Ana and she told me how she spelt it cos it didn't sound like Ana. I told her that her name was a pantomime or something like that cos her name can be said frontwards or backwards and still sound the same. On the way back I would see Toma again and buy another energy ice cream and he would always give me two scoops on the way home although he only charged me for one. By the time I got back to the house I had eaten the ice cream and would go in and get all the breakfast ready and then everyone would appear. They would all be stretching and yawning even though it was about nine o'clock. Mummy and daddy got a cup of coffee cos Skip had taught us how to do that. I would get orange juice ready and afterwards I would wash up the plates and things whilst mummy and daddy and Matthew were washing up themselves. Then I would sweep the floor and tidy my bed then get my stuff ready for the beach or wherever we were going. Mummy said to me every morning that I was such a good little boy and give me more kuna. I love being helpful and on holiday I was just glad that I could be so much use.

One evening we were strolling (that's what daddy said we were doing) along the marina after we had had dinner and mummy asked me and Matthew if we would like an ice cream and I knew what I wanted and Matthew had to look. After a minute he said that he would like an energy ice cream. Mummy then asked Toma what was in it and he said Red Bull and mummy said that Matthew couldn't have it. Then I asked if I could and mummy said no and Toma smiled and said, "Sorry, Alex" and mummy asked me how he knew my name so I told her that I walked past him every morning (twice) and said "Hallo." I had a pink one instead. Then Toma told mummy that he gave me a slag every day as well and daddy spluttered and mummy just said, "Really, no wonder Alex is so cheerful when he comes back with the cross aunts." I just smiled.

Mummy likes to take it easy on holiday, according to daddy but so does he according to me, so when I saw that where we were staying had a dishwasher I knew what I had to do. When I went out with daddy one morning there was a man by the harbour selling fish which he said was called see bream. Daddy bought four and I said that I would cook them. So mummy bought some salady bits and potatoes and I was left alone in the kitchen. I boiled the potatoes and put them in a bowl with some chives and mayo and cut the salad bits up and did the same with some walnut oil and then I put the fish in the dishwasher (with the dirty plates that mummy and daddy had put in during the day, so as not to waste hot water) and put the dishwasher on start. I didn't realise that dishwashers take so long but when it finally finished there wasn't much left of the fish, just the bones and some innards. Mummy went mad and said that it was a stupid sweary idea and so I told her that Bendy had done it in France Italy and the salmon was yummy but she said that Bendy had probably wrapped the salmon in three layers of foil and put the machine on a rinse cycle, whatever that is. But how was I to know? Anyway I said that I would eat it and then mummy said that I was supposed to gut the fish and take the innards out but how was I to know that as well? So I had a few bits of fish and some skin and it was okay but a bit lemony and when I told mummy she said that that was because she had put a sweary dishwasher tablet in earlier and then I cried cos it's hard work trying to be a Chief Scout and I don't know if I can ever be an adult cos there seems to be so much that you need to know and then mummy cuddled me and we had pizza.

## Friday 4th September
**Alex**
Back to Scouts, thank goodness and time for a bit of chef badge. Skip had emailed our mummies to tell them we would be eating so not to feed us too much. When we arrived at Scouts the campfire was already burning well. Skip said that it takes about an hour for a good cooking fire to be lit and then to burn down to embers. This means that in our two-hour troop meeting, once you have put some time aside for clearing up and washing up (i.e. nearly an hour if Joe's involved), if the fire isn't lit beforehand then we

would have about 5 minutes for cooking which would mean not much more than a sosage, and a skinny one at that. No one likes a skinny sosage.

Skip told us about the different coloured chopping boards for different foods. There's red for meat, blue for fish, white for dairy and yellow for bananas I think. We only have one at home and it's wood. So I've probably got loads of germs inside me but they haven't killed me yet.

We have a new Scout that has joined us. He is twelve but he has been a Scout before. He comes from Croatia where I was on holiday. I don't think that he followed us home. His name is Tin so we call him Can. He has moved here to live which is a bit odd when they have such lovely ice cream in Croatia. I asked him what "Slag" was and he said, "Whipped cream." And I said, "Oh." Of course Can wanted to know why but I couldn't really explain. I asked him if he knew Ana in the bakery at Milna and he said that he didn't. He brought along a small lump of meat that he said was from where he was born. That is Croatia as well. Can told us that everyone is very poor where he comes from so they eat everything. I expect he means innards and stuff like that. This isn't a problem to Scouts who are used to surviving on food in the wild. When Skip asked him what the lump of meat was he said that he didn't know what it was in English, he did know it was a small animal, but he said that he knew what it was in Croatian, obviously. Cos he's not going to go into the butchers and just ask for meat is he? He then got out his phone and said that he could ring his mummy and ask her which was stupid cos Can's mummy doesn't speak much English, according to Can, so she's just going to say what it is in Croation. Anyway cos Can got out his phone Skip confiscated it which is what he always does cos no phones at Scouts. Skip then said that he could write the name on the whiteboard so we could try and guess cos it might be okay cos Can said in Croation that a banana is a banana and so Can picked up the large red whiteboard pen and wrote

P U H

across the board in big letters. "It's pooh," said Barnaby. "I knew it. Can's going to make us eat pooh. Bear Grills has eaten pooh and now we are going to have to." "And how do you pronounce that, Can?" asked Skip who was ignoring Barnaby, as usual. And Skip sighed a sigh of relief when Can said, "like POOF." "So now we're going to eat a poof!" said guess who? Then Skip got really cross and told Barnaby to shut up only all the Scouts were giggling so Barnaby just smiled. Then Can said that his mummy had got it all ready and all we had to do was varm it up in a sospan, which is what we did. Can was put in charge of warming up his poof but he also got his hands on some frozen Wagon Wheels that Skip got out to defrost so he put those in the sospan first and made a bit of a mess. I think he thought they were burgers. He then wanted to know where the tomato catchup was and we all laughed while he looked puzzled.

When we were eating pudding Ken came to speak to us. Ken helps at Explorers and he is like my Action Man, all dressed up in camouflage and with big muscles like Popeye. He's mad. He came to speak to the Scouts that were moving up to Explorers soon so that they would know what to expect. He told us about all the things that he had shot, skinned, gutted and eaten. Ken has eaten a crocodile but even he didn't know what a poof was when Barnaby asked him, although he smiled and said something to Skip so maybe he does know he was just not letting on. Then he told us about some of the places he had been to and he said that he had been hunting in Bosnia. It was a great story but we all knew it wasn't true cos Bosnia isn't a country, we all knew that. Except Can who said that it was a country, but what does he know?

While the cooking was going on we played some campfire games. And we played The Enlarging Machine where we throw things over a sheet and they come back bigger and at the end we throw over a cup of water and back comes a bucketful to soak someone who doesn't know what's going to happen but we had a load of old fire extinguishers and Gunner had one and let it off over Skip and he was soaked so he had to take off his trousers and wear a towel and he then had to dry his trousers by the campfire but forgot that he had Can's phone in his pocket. Then it was time to go home and Can wasn't allowed his phone back which is mean cos Skip always gives phones back and Skip told the parents that he was wearing a Scout kilt.

Barnaby wore his hiking boots to Scouts tonight. The melted soles have reset so it looks like he's standing in a black puddle all the time and when he walks it looks like the puddle is following him. He's going to tell his mummy that his soles melted cos the camp fire was too hot cos she doesn't know yet. This will mean that Skip will get into trouble and not Barnaby.

**Friday 11th September**
**Alex**
Tonight was not a good night at Scouts. First of all we were

doing flag break, being all solemn and quiet, except Barnaby, when Can came in with his mummy who is called Tea-ah. I know this cos Skip saw her come in and said very quietly, "Oh hello Tea-ah. Can I speak to you at the end of the meeting?" But no, Tea-ah was not going to wait. "What you done Tin phone, why can not he have back?" which sounded like English to me. Skip said that phones weren't allowed at Scout meetings (good) but Skip always gave them back at the end. Skip said that there was a problem with Can's phone and that he would have to speak to Tea-ah later and then she said that she was not eppy especially as she ad given Can a culinree specialitee for Scouts last week to eat at the camp fire. Skip then said, "Ah yes, what is 'poof'?" and Tea-ah said it's emster and when Skip said "Hamster?" and Tea-ah said, "Yes, fat emster" then Laura burst into tears again and was then really sick - again. I can't think why, after all it's not going to be her emster. Although I suppose it may be a son or daughter or something. Anyway, she didn't eat any, but we did.

## Friday 18th September
**Alex**

Big news tonight! Tegan has won first prize in a junior running competition at Crystal Palace. She got a tiny medal which she wore around her neck all evening. She said that she thought that it was worth more than a mouldy old medal so she's added her name to a list of record holders of the fastest one hundred metres on Wikipedia. I wonder how long it will be before they find out?

## Friday 25th September
**Alex**

Tegan is still a record holder.

## Friday 2nd October
### Alex

Another Scout night, another badge. Skip has given us all a pound and told us to go and make some money as part of the Fundraising badge. We discussed some ideas and had a brain steaming session. A lot of ideas seem to be around food. Food sells! I'm going to make cookies at half-term. We have to bring our money back after half-term and have a debrief which is a talk about what we did. Tegan is no longer a record holder. At least she was for two weeks which is more than most.

## Saturday 17th October
### Alex

Today we had a trip to Dover. We visited the castle which was really interesting. The insides of the castle were used during the Second World War. Gunner was helping. I expect he worked there during the war. We then hiked to a lighthouse along the White Cliffs of Dover. We went up to the top of it and it was really windy. Then we had a bit of a rest and we had all brought our water bottles. But Barnaby wasn't drinking out of his and when Skip asked him why not he said, "Well, I didn't know that we were supposed to put water in them." Then we hiked back and got a hikes away tick. It should have taken four hours to get a tick but we hiked quickly because we knew what was coming. Skip still gave us a tick though. In the afternoon we went to a factory where they made rock. They had allowed us to help make some. You have to roll out the coloured outside, then the inside and then put the wording in and then cut it up and put it in cellofane. Jake was meant to get HASTINGS in the word bit but when Skip wasn't looking Jake asked the man if he could put BULLOCKS in the rock because his best friend's daddy is a farmer but he had to do it quickly so no one would notice. Sadly for Jake he got really told off cos once the rock had cooled down and we had cellofaned it and put a Welcome to Hastings label in all of the pieces one of the rock people noticed that all the rock that we had done had BOLLOCKS written in it, which is nothing much to do with farmers, and so two thousand pieces of rock had to be uncellofaned, unlabelled and melted down to start again. Skip said it would have been okay if Jake's friend's daddy was a banker, but he isn't. Anyway, all's well that ends well. Jake managed to hide five sticks of BOLLOCKS rock and he took it home. He did pay for it though but he had to tell the girl in the shop bit that he was making a contribution so that she wouldn't be suspicious.

## Friday 23rd October
### Skip
Another big gap in the diary, sorry, but I've been busy trying to sort out a visit from an Australian Scout. His name is Jimmy and he comes from Tasmania. There's a group of Aussie Scouts coming over for the month of December and I've volunteered to put one up. Should be fun. Mind you, I can't quite understand why the Aussies want to leave behind their summer sun to come and find our winter cold, but hey-ho, we'll make him welcome.

## Friday 23rd October
### Alex
Half-term so no Scout meeting. Mummy bought some nut and chocolate cookie ingredients and I made them. It was a lot of hard work and I'm not sure if I got all the ingredients right or the cooker stuff but they looked okay in the end.

Mummy said that I should wait until they had cooled down considerably before I went out and sold them. Mummy said I could sell them tomorrow.

## Saturday 24th October
**Alex**

Cookie day! After a night of cooling down the cookies looked much better and were now the shape that I thought they should be. Hugo came round and we went up the road to sell them. We sold them all in about one hour. We went to Mr xxxxx next door and he bought a load and when we were walking further up the road we saw nosey Mrs xxxxx, his wife, who asked us what we were doing. When we told her she said that she would buy some. So we sold her some as well. Serves her right for being nosey. I then went and bought some more ingredients and made even more. I'm going to sell them at Scouts.

## Sunday 25th October
**Alex**

Cookies are go! These new ones didn't settle very well like the first lot so I broke them into bits and put them in a tin ready for the big sale at Scouts on Friday.

## Friday 30th October
**Alex**

Our fundraising badge debrief took place tonight. It all started with a bit of an adventure. None of the Scouts wanted to buy my cookie bits so I gave them away at the drinks break. Barnaby had a handful and then went red and started coughing and gasping. Skip came running over and asked what he had drunk. I told him that he had had orange squash and Alex's famous cookie bits. He then wanted to know what was in them. This I knew so I told him. Each batch contained ten ounces of flour, six ounces of butter and so on. When I said at the end, cos I had forgotten and it was important cos they're healthy, "AND a LOAD of Brazil nuts," Skip freaked out, then stabbed Barnaby with a pen and we had to call an ambulance. Skip said that Barnaby had had an Anna somebody shock. It was all a bit distressing. I didn't think my cookies were that bad. I hope Mrs xxxxx is okay. At least she paid for hers.

Once things had calmed down and Skip had calmed down we had our debrief. In total we raised nearly a thousand pounds of which yours truly contributed £47.36. Sarah-Jane and Trudy had put their money together and bought some ingredients then made some biscuits which they sold and then bought loads of ingredients and put leaflets through doors saying "Freshly made cakes, any flavour". Then, as the orders came in they made the cakes and delivered them the same day. They made £120.46 which means that they will probably win a prize. Jake said that he had set up a pop-up cafe in his road and sold all sorts of home-made biscuits. They also had a raffle. The first prize was a Bear Grills book which he had signed and which raised loads of money. Jake told me that the only problem was that it wasn't signed by Bear Grills, it was signed by Jake. Second prize was a stick of bollocks rock. Third prize was an ipad and fourth prize was an X-box (which the Explorers call a Y-bother box). Jake raised £195.00. I'm not sure why the rock was second prize. It may be quite original but an ipad would have to be worth more. Sophie said that she used her one pound as a guarantee for another pound from her mummy. She then lent the two pounds to her sister and charged her a fee of three pounds, so on pocket money day she got five pounds.

She then expanded her empire and ended up making over twenty pounds and she didn't even have to make anything. Some of the Scouts did nothing with their one pound and just brought them back with a sorry. Lee said that he couldn't do anything because he had been away. One boy, it had to be Tyler, misunderstood the whole thing completely and spent the one pound on sweets, which he then ate. He won't be getting a badge.

Barnaby put his brother on EBay. Then it was taken down, but not before he had raised three pounds. Now Barnaby's brother is going round telling everyone that at least he's not worthless although at three pounds he's hardly priceless either.

**Friday 6th November**
**Alex**
Jake has doubled the fundraising total! He has put another piece of bollocks rock on EBay and it raised a thousand pounds. Well done Jake. Skip has put Jake forward for a Jack Petchey community award for services to Scouting. I wonder what it will say on his certificate?

Tonight we brain steamed what to spend the fundraising money on. Most of us were in complete agreement - more tents! Some wanted a trampoline but I think that that was just the girls getting together to try and influence Skip. I don't think he's the sort of person that will be influenced by a few girls, although there are quite a few girls in 3rd Chislehurst. Most of the girls were Brownies who didn't want to be guides, apart from Trudy. She was a Brownie who wasn't allowed to be a Guide, probably for telling tales.

Then there was what Skip called a seminar moment. Sarah suggested that we give ten percent of the money to charity. Skip said this was a fabulous idea and he would research some suitable charities. I reckon a charity for retired Skips would be a good idea, so I told him. Skip said that it made him sound like a rusty industrial waste bin although I don't know why.

**Friday 13th November**
**Alex**
A charity decision has been made. We're going to give some money to the local special school and we're going to sponsor a toilet for those in the Third World that don't have one. This means twinning our Scout toilet through www.toilettwinning.com. I would have thought that we could have started by twinning with some local Scout camp sites.

We went and picked slows this evening in Scadbury Park. They didn't taste very nice. Skip said that they needed to be frozen and then we can make some slow jam at Scouts. That would be fun! Our own home-made jam with hand-picked fruit. That's what I call survival!

I sent Chloe a text yesterday to say that I hope she's okay. I got one back that said, "Our present sufferings are not worth comparing with the glory that will be revealed in us." Has she gone mad? I don't know what she's talking about. No one seems to know. Maybe I should ask Skip but he doesn't say anything so I'm a bit afraid to ask.

**Friday 13th November**
**Skip**

Sorry, Diary, that I've been neglecting you but I've been rather tied up with Chloe. However, Scouts continues apace and we've been up to loads of things since the summer. I took the Scouts round Scadbury Park this evening and we picked four kilos of sloes. I told them that we would make jam with them but I've brought them home and stuck them in the freezer. There's enough there to make around ten litres of sloe gin. I just need to get some gin first. It's a pity I can't get the Scouts to distil some. They'ld enjoy that.

## Friday 20th November
## Alex

We're having a bring and buy book sale next week. Lee said that he would get some out of the library. I hope we've not got a thief in Scouts, it's bad enough with Josh's dad. Anyway, I use our local library, so I hope that Lee will not be taking the books from there. It's very useful and I can borrow as many books as I like with my library card. So, hands off Lee!

## Friday 27th November
## Alex

Our toilet has been twinned. Skip brought in a certificate which had a photo of our twinned toilet in Pakistan and has our name on it. It's a very nice, grey, brick built toilet in a place called Marriyamabad. It looks like it's in the middle of a field. Skip said that he is going to send a photo of our Scout Hut toilet to Pakistan with a request that they hang it in their toilet that we're sponsoring. Trudy said that theirs looks nicer than our own Scout Hut toilet so maybe they should be sending us some money. Our toilet has spiders. They probably don't have spiders in Pakistan. But they will have snakes. Imagine being on the toilet and a snake comes in cos the door doesn't go down to the floor. What would you do? I would be alright cos I would be prepared and I would have my Swiss Army knife in my pocket. But Sarah wouldn't be prepared so she would probably be bitten. That would be a bit of a mess! Imagine going in to the toilet and getting rid of a poo but picking up a snake bite? Still, it wouldn't happen to Sarah cos she's nice and she's the one who suggested buying a toilet so she would probably by okay though. Anyway, she said that she doesn't ever poo in public toilets, only private ones which must be a bit of a problem if she goes shopping what with mummies and girls going for shopping for a whole day at a time. Not Joe, though. Joe would be eaten, especially if a lion came in. I wonder if they use toilet paper in Pakistan? We ran out tonight. Skip wasn't happy. We were playing a game of mummies where you have to wrap your Petrol Leader or Assistant Petrol Leader up in toilet paper so that only their eyes and nose show and then they have to walk, or shuffle more like, to the end of the Scout Hut and back again without breaking any of the paper. However, as soon as the mummies were ready, Tegan said that she was desperate to go to the toilet. Skip told her that she didn't have to ask and that she could just go but then Tegan said that she wanted to do a poo but there was no toilet paper cos I had stolen it for Woodpecker's mummy. How was I to know that we were only allowed one roll each? No one said. I thought I was using my initiative in borrowing some more. Anyway, we had to unwrap enough sheets from Josh so that Tegan could go to the poo with a bit to spare by which time Josh's head was completely exposed and so we were disqualified. Anyway, all's well that ends well cos Tegan said that she had a very good poo and Josh said that he was relieved that Tegan had used the toilet paper after it had been round his head and not before.

I brought in a load of unwanted books. So did Lee. But I knew that they weren't from Chislehurst Library as they had no label inside so I reckoned that Lee hadn't stolen them. So I asked him which library he had stolen them from. He didn't look very happy and said that he hadn't stolen them from any public library. He had got them from his dad's library and his dad had said that he could take a few and that his dad had given him some. How was I to know that Lee's dad had his own library? I should've guessed, what with his dad being a banker. Most of us have to go down to Chislehurst library with a card to get some books. Even then you can only keep them for three weeks then you have to take them back. So the only library we have at our house is one with about five books, and they change every month.

## Saturday 28th November
### Skip
Our bring and buy book sale went well today with a number of books brought and sold. Unfortunately Lee's books went unsold as no one was particularly interested in titles such as Banking in a Globalised World or The Mystery of Banking.

## Friday 4th December
### Alex
Our last camp of the year. We're having it in the Scout Hut grounds and in tents so it's a bit cold. Skip said that we need to have four seasons sleeping bags which means that we can camp when it's freezing. It wasn't freezing, though, it was just very wet. We had two new girls, Rhianna and Mimi, who were Brownies, but who don't want to be Guides, to visit before camp time. They came with their mummies. We were having a baby food eating competition. Skip had

bought loads of jars of baby food and we were going to empty it into billies to cook on the camp fire. We had chicken curry, apple pie and stuff like that. Unfortunately Akela had taken all the billies home to clean them and all we had was some silver foil. We made some foil containers using three sheets and wrapped up the baby food. We mixed the main meals in together and then the puddings and put it all on the embers. After a few minutes we opened up the foil and attacked the contents with our spoons. It was at this moment the new parents arrived and asked us what we were doing. When Skip said that we were eating baby food one of the new parents said that maybe we should be eating something more substantial. Barnaby said that it was always what we had on camp as Skip didn't allow us to use a knife to chop stuff up. It was at this point that Rhianna's mummy tried to take Rhianna home, but Rhianna refused so Rhianna stayed with Mimi and Mimi's mummy and they all tucked in.

At the end of the evening when it was time to put the embers of the camp fire to bed, Skip asked me and said that as we were in a bit of a rush we should use hot water as it puts the fire out quicker. He then said that I needed to wash some wood for breakfast as it always burns better when it's clean. I'm glad that he asked me cos he knows I'm a top Scout even though I'm still only in my first year - just. I said, "I know, I'm not a Guide who knows nothing, I'm a Scout" and he just smiled. Then Rhianna and Mimi smiled. Rhianna and Mimi won't be Chief Scouts as they're girls. Skip knows that one day I'll be Chief Scout so he has to respect me otherwise I will sack him. I wonder how much he gets paid? Quite a bit I reckon.

## Saturday 5th December
### Alex

At breakfast Jake said that he didn't feel well and was then sick over the camp fire which I had only just got going. It took rather a long time to get it going again after that by which time no one felt very hungry. I made a teepee using Try Kissing Lotte (yuch) but it was all a bit of an effort even though I had washed all the wood. I even soaked the tinder overnight so that I knew that it would be really clean. Oh gosh. I am so confused. I thought that tinder was supposed to be dry. Am I ever going to be a good Scout? Laura said that as Jake was sicking up food we could just pick at it with a fork once the fire got going and eat it again. It would be like recycling food. Just imagine how cheap food could be if we all ate it and then sicked it up and then ate it again. Everything would be so much cheaper. Jake is a pig. He was sick because last night Aaron betted him that he wouldn't eater a firelighter and he did! Had Jake not been sick I could have told Jake to breathe out as I lit a match. That would have got the fire started! He would be 3rd Chislehurst's official St George. St George breathed fire. I asked Hugo how much his daddy gets paid for being a Scout leader and he said that he didn't know but it would be quite a lot as it takes up quite a bit of his time specially as how he has to do everything, even clean up sick.

## Friday 11th December
### Alex

Jake has been to a special Children of Endeavour dinner evening run by the local Council cos of all the fundraising money that he raised for 3rd Chislehurst. When the mayor was asking everyone what they had done, Jake said that he had been fundraising. When the mayor asked him what was his fundraising, Jake said that he had sold a stick of rock on EBay. When the mayor said that it must have been a very special piece of rock, Jake told him that it was bollocks and the mayor went red and Jake had to go home early.

**Friday 18th December**
**Alex**
Our last Scouts this year cos next Friday is Christmas Day and then it's New Year's Day. Chloe wasn't at Scouts tonight again. I hope she's alright. Mummy asked me what I would like for Christmas and I said that I would like a penknife and she said that I had one and I said that I want a waterproof one and she said that they are all made of stainless steal and are all waterproof. So I don't know what Barnaby was talking about when we were raft-building.

**Friday 18th December**
**Skip**
It's the comment that every parent dreads. Today, at lunch, Charlie [Hugo's older brother] said, "I have something to tell you, daddy." "Oh, what's that?" I asked, barely registering the sound of anxiety in his voice. "I'm not sure how to tell you, daddy." I put down my newspaper, looked Charlie in the eye and said, "Just tell me." "I don't think I can." I was starting to get worried. What couldn't he tell me? He was always happy to tell me about what was going on in his life. "Does Lucy-Jane know?" I asked anxiously. "Yes." I turned to Lucy-Jane. "Well, I'm not telling you daddy. It's for Charlie to tell you." By now I was getting really concerned. Was my sixteen year old son gay? Was he not gay? Was his girlfriend pregnant? I didn't even know that he had a girlfriend. "It's okay, Charlie," I said finally. "There's no rush. Just tell me when you're ready." "Thanks dad." We

carried on with our meal and then Charlie suddenly piped up again, "I'm ready to tell you now." And I was ready for the worst. "Okay, Charlie, what is it?" I asked gently. He looked at me sheepishly. "Yesterday, I used your razor; I had a shave." "Was that all it was?" I asked. "Yes, daddy. But I thought you might be cross." In the afternoon I went out and bought Charlie the biggest and most expensive turbo-charged, multi-headed dual-speed electric razor that I could find. "Thanks, dad," Charlie said when I gave it to him later on. "Now, daddy, there's just one more thing I need to tell you." "It can wait," I said to Charlie. "I need to save up."

## Friday 25th December
## Alex

Christmas Day and I've got a few really nice presents. We had a church parade in the morning which 3rd Chislehurst does every Christmas and it was great. The vicar had a big box of sweets and he said that if anyone had anything to celebrate we could come up and get a sweet. Barnaby got up and whispered, "Follow me," so we all did and there were about thirty of us. The vicar gave us all a sweet and when we had sat down he said, "What are you all celebrating and Barnaby said, "Jesus' birthday!" and we all laughed and everyone else in the church was laughing and the vicar was laughing and then he said, "Oh sweary it! Let's all have a sweet!" and if it's someone's birthday next week they're probably not going to get a sweet cos we've scoffed them all.

Chloe didn't come to parade so I kept my sweet for her and I will take it round to her house in the next few days. I sent her a Happy Christmas text and all I got back was a "†". What does it all mean?

## Friday 25th December
## Skip

Jimmy's given me as a present a rugby ball. Not any old rugby ball, it is in fact an Australian rules football. Fantastic. I said to Jimmy that we would pump it up and have a play whilst the rest of the family watches the Queen. I asked Hugo what pressure to pump it to and he said that it said on the ball, "inflate to 45." 45 psi is quite high as it's what I put in my bike tyres, but what do I know? Off I went with the bike pump - pump, pump, pump as the boys stood round watching in the comfort of our sitting room, with everyone else looking on. I stopped at exactly 45 and withdrew the needle. "It's a bit solid." I said to Jimmy, "Do you normally play with it this hard?" Jimmy took it and bounced it on the travertine floor. He bounced it like a pro, so that it would come back into his hands, but even so it bounced over his shoulder. "It's not normally this bouncy, but maybe it's just because it's new," he drawled, as he went and retrieved it from Auntie Ruth who had taken a fine catch in one hand without moving, with the other hand still grasping a large Tia Maria and with her eyes on Her Majesty. "Here, let me have a go," said Hugo. He took the ball and bounced it straight down on the floor. It shot straight up, hit the low ceiling and then, "BANG!" The cats shot off the sofa, Hugo screamed, and granny's Tia Maria was no more, to the detriment of Lucy-Jane who was sitting next to her. The ball's innards had exploded and had taken with it most of the upper half's stitching. The innards were sticking out like a take on the Rolling Stone's iconic tongue logo. "Oh dear," said Hugo. "Very funny, Jimmy," I said to him, in a desperate attempt to calm everyone down. "We have joke golf balls in this country that explode when they're hit. You have a joke football. I should have known. It is, after all,

294

quite a funny size." "It's supposed to be that size, and it not a joke. I bought it from a sports shop." "In that case, why did it blow up?" Then grandad intervened. "What did you blow it up to?" "45 psi, like Hugo said," I said, quickly passing any buck that was coming my way. "Let me have a look," said grandad, taking hold of what was left of the ball. He put on his glasses and read, "Lubricate needle. Inflate to 45 kpa." He put down his glasses and said, "I don't know what 'kpa' is, probably, 'kilos per' something, but it's not 'pounds per square inch,' that's for sure. Do you know, Jimmy?" "Yeah, it's 'kilopascal.'" "And what's 45 kilopascals in psi?" "It would probably be about six." "So there's your answer, John," he said as he threw me 'the ball'. "You've pumped up the ball to the equivalent of about 300 psi on your bike tyre."

## Sunday 27th December
## Skip
A great but busy Christmas. My best present, apart from the ball, has to be a paraffin heater for the greenhouse. New year's eve party, here I come!

## Thursday 31st December
## Alex
New Year's Eve! Hurrah! Mummy and daddy are going out to a party with Skip and Hugo's mummy – again! I thought that he would've learnt his lesson! Matthew's gone round to his girlfriend's and guess who's coming round here in a few minutes? I'll tell you tomorrow, Mr Diary!

To be continued...

So, who is Alex having round? Why was everyone patting

their heads in Italy? What is the matter with Chloe? Find out the answers and more in the third in the series, "Dear Skip. Letters to a Scout Leader" to be published soon.

If you've enjoyed "Sleeping Bags & Tortures" then don't forget to read, if you haven't already done so, "In You Go! A Year or Two in the Life of a Scout Leader" which is the first book in the series.

# DEDICATION

*See page 163

In 2011, when I was fairly certain, in Scouting at least, that I was trying to run before I could walk, I went on a training weekend for one of my modules. It was one that was aimed at those Scout leaders that wanted to take their young people on a nights away event; that is to say, in the main, camping. In Scouting it's not a case of just thinking one day, "Oooh, I fancy going camping with the kids," and off you go. There is planning to be done, menus, a programme, admin., budgeting. You have to know yourself how to light a fire (without petrol), you have to learn a few songs and skits to perform round the camp fire and you have to know what to do when x, y or z happens (because they will happen). On this weekend I met Ben Richardson who, I think I'm right in saying, had just become the County Commissioner for Greater London South East and although was a far more experienced Scouter than I could ever be had still, even though he really had no need to, decided to bring himself along to this "camping module" weekend to see how our county "did it." It was a weekend where we rookie Cub and Scout leaders were effectively Scouts, going through a weekend camp, but with beer and fags and a couple of late nights. (Nothing different there then especially so far as the late nights were concerned, but ours were round the camp fire with a Fosters and not in a tent after lights should have been out with a, er, Fosters.) I had already regaled both the other leaders and our instructors with a day in my life that I need bore no one with here, but it's in the notorious Chapter Seven of "In You Go! A year or two in the life of a Scout leader" if you're interested.

At about one o'clock on the Sunday morning, when no one appeared ever to be going to bed, Ben brought out his phone and showed me a video of "When Zippy and George do 'Top Gear'" which is, by the producers' own admission, a "pretty twisted take on a classic TV show" and which was made as a spoof Top Gear for Jeremy Clarkson's birthday, when he was still fronting Top Gear for the BBC. It is described as, "Zippy & George try their hand at presenting with cars, girls and endless puns!" It is not for the faint-hearted. In one scene one of the protagonists admits that his name is Lager Fanny, again for reasons that shall, within the context of this dedication, remain unclear. Ben loved this bit, gruffling and gigging as he rewound several times so as to ensure that no one watching over his shoulder had missed a word or frame.

Despite Chapter Seven I passed my module and despite Lager Fanny, Ben kept his position before moving on.

Some months later, at a St George's Day Parade at Bromley High School, which was the first to be held since Bromley District had expanded to become the biggest district in the country, and therefore could no longer be held in a church building, but now in a playing field, I found myself marching past the gathered worthies at the front. There, centre stage, was Ben, and before I could stop myself, I found that I was miming Lager Fanny to him across the no man's land. Ben was not a person to take such things lying down so he looked me in the eye, and from fifty feet away, in the presence of Bob Neill MP, James Cleverly Member of the London Assembly, various past presidents et al, stuck his finger in my direction in his best Lord Kitchener impersonation and shouted, "I've got more on you, mate!" As I turned back all I could see was the most enormous grin on his face as the march-past continued. It was one-nil to Ben.

Despite meeting Ben on several occasions after this I never managed to make it one-all, so I've now had to make do with one of my characters saying, "I've got more on you, mate!" just for Ben. For his cheery smile and love for life were cut short far too soon. My prayer is that this dedication will, in some small way, let those who loved him most know that he is sorely missed.

Rest in Peace mate.

## ALSO AVAILABLE BY JOHN HEMMING-CLARK

### In You Go!
### A Year or Two in the Life of a Scout Leader

**ISBN:** 978 1 897864 26 5
**Price:** £9.99 paperback
**Published:** Searchline Publishing
Searchline House, Holbrook Lane, Chislehurst, BR7 6PE
**Tel & Fax:** +44 (0)20 8295 0739

**www.inyougo.webeden.co.uk**
**www.amazon.co.uk**

Dragged into Scouting as a result of his son having no Scout leader locally, John Hemming-Clark soon found that, far from being dead on its legs, Scouting was in robust good health with over one hundred years of resource behind it.

Soon his Scout section was full up and John found himself a first-hand witness to what the youngsters of today get up to, what they say and what they do, whether it be at troop meeting, camp, hike or other Scouting activity.

At times hilarious and at others touching, John recounts episodes of not only Scouts at play, but also leaders, trainers, helpers and the other Scout sections as well as the Girl Guides that John's Scouts came across from time to time, with insights from his past that brought him into Scouting at a time when most are thinking of putting their feet up.

*"...this is one of the funniest books I have ever read."*
*Amazon review*

# ALSO AVAILABLE BY JOHN HEMMING-CLARK

## 1000 Fantastic Scout Games

**ISBN:** 978 1 897864 29 6
**Price:** £9.99 paperback
**Published:** Searchline Publishing
Searchline House, Holbrook Lane, Chislehurst, BR7 6PE
**Tel & Fax:** +44 (0)20 8295 0739

**www.inyougo.webeden.co.uk**
**www.amazon.co.uk**

As leaders of children, be they Scouts, Guides, members of after-school clubs, churches or youth groups, we already have the commitment to ensure that, as much as we are able, those in our charge have the opportunity for games that will stimulate and challenge, leading to happier and healthier children.

If you struggle to come up with original, fun and stimulating games for your young people, or are just looking for some new ideas, then 1,000 Fantastic Scout Games is for you. Designed for Scouts, but appropriate for children of any age or persuasion, you will never be without a fantastic game idea.

*"Great book, fantastic to have so many games to hand ..."*

*"A lot of new ideas covering indoor and outdoor games with easy to follow instructions. I highly recommend this to any Scout or play groups and is suitable for all sections and ages." Amazon reviews*

# The Ultimate Triathlon
By James Ketchell

www.jamesketchell.net

The Ultimate Triathlon is a work of non-fiction based on James' experiences and journey to become the only person in history to complete what the media dubbed the 'Ultimate Triathlon'.